# THE LITTLE

The fascinating and amazingly
delightful world of mathematics.
Fun, Simple, Witty, Logical, Absorbing.

# BOOK OF

Open this entertaining book
anywhere and learn from it.

# MATHS

Small minds discuss persons.
Average minds discuss events.
Great minds discuss ideas. Really
great minds discuss mathematics.

∞

## The Author

SURENDRA VERMA is a science journalist and author based in Melbourne. His recent popular science books are: *The Mystery of the Tunguska Fireball, The Little Book of Scientific Principles, Theories & Things; Why Aren't They Here?: The Question of Life on Other Worlds* and *The Cause of Mosquitoes' Sorrow: Beginnings, Blunders and Breakthroughs in Science.*

## Praise for Surendra Verma's Other Books

### *The Little Book of Scientific Principles, Theories & Things*

'Verma writes with wit and clear enjoyment, demystifying the most difficult concepts.'

*The Good Book Guide*

'Verma's remarkable little book combines hard practical worth with history and fun.'

*Cosmos*

### *Why Aren't They Here?: The Question of Life on Other Worlds*

'A masterpiece of science writing and journalism — in-your-face, direct and beautifully written ... a gem of wisdom, scholarship and fun.'

*BBC Focus*

'A calm, intelligent and witty survey of the history of mankind's search for extraterrestrial life.'

*Daily Mail*

# THE LITTLE
# BOOK OF
# MATHS
# THEOREMS,
# THEORIES
# &THINGS

SURENDRA VERMA

Orient
Publishing

DELHI | MUMBAI | HYDERABAD

ISBN : 978-81-222-0415-5

*The Little Book of Maths Theorems, Theories & Things*

Subject: Education / Maths / Recreation

© Surendra Verma, 2008

1st Published 2010
5th Printing 2013

Published in arrangement with
New Holland Publishers (Australia) Pty Ltd

Published by
**Orient Publishing**
(an imprint of Orient Paperbacks)
5A/8 Ansari Road, New Delhi-110 002
www.orientpublishing.com

Cover Design by Vision Studio

Printed at
Saurabh Printers Pvt. Ltd., Noida, India

Cover Printed at
Ravindra Printing Press, Delhi-110 006, India

# Contents

Answers to puzzles

$\mathcal{M}$athematics is the world's best game.
It is more absorbing than chess, more engaging than poker,
and lasts longer than Monopoly. It's free. It can be played
anywhere — Archimedes did it in a bathtub!

Richard J. Trudeau,
*Dots and Lines*

# Introduction

Somebody came up to Ralph P. Boas, Jr (1912-92), a distinguished American mathematician, after a talk he had given, and said, 'You make mathematics seem like fun.' Boas was inspired to reply: 'If it isn't fun, why do it?'

Mathematics is indeed fun as this little book testifies. This book presents a unique collection of mathematical ideas, theories, theorems, conjectures, rules, facts, equations, formulas, paradoxes, fallacies and puzzles with short, simple and witty explanations that require no background in mathematics. It is peppered with anecdotes, quotes, limericks and poems showing the quirky and amusing side of mathematics and of people who have added, in the words of Roger Bacon (1214-92), 'things to this world which cannot be made known without knowledge of mathematics'.

Get ready for a fascinating walk through mathematics.

The essence of mathematics
is not to make simple things complicated,
but to make complicated things simple.

S. Gudder

# From infinity to divinity

In mathematics, infinity is a number — although the weirdest one we know.

We use the word infinite to describe something that is endless, limitless and unbounded.

Infinity is a mind-boggling concept, especially for us who live in a closed, finite universe which has a finite number of atoms. Some scientists estimate this number to be of the order of $10^{81}$ (1 followed by 81 zeros), which is less than one googol (see p. 139).

The famous 'paradox of the Grand Hotel' devised by the German mathematician David Hilbert (1862-1943) provides a peek into the weird world of infinity.

Hilbert's hotel has an infinity number of rooms all lined up in an endless corridor and numbered 1, 2, 3,... forever. One night all its rooms are occupied, yet the 'Vacancy' sign is still on. A new guest arrives and asks for a room. 'No worries,' smiles the wily proprietor and he moves the guest occupying Room 1 into Room 2, the occupant of Room 2 into Room 3, and so on. He now asks the new guest to move to Room 1, which becomes vacant when all his guests have moved to their new rooms.

Next night a tourist bus, with an infinite number of tourists on board, arrives at the hotel. 'No worries,' shouts the proprietor. 'Just wait a minute.' With infinite patience he moves the guest in Room 1 into Room 2, the guest in Room 2 to Room 4, the guest into Room 3 into Room 6, and so on, leaving all the odd-numbered rooms vacant for the infinite number of newly arrived guests.

Hotel Infinity will not ever run out of rooms for an infinite number of tourist buses, each packed with infinite number of tourists, if they all arrive at the same time. In the world of infinity, a part can be equal to the whole.

The British astrophysicist Arthur Eddington (1882-1944) was no fan of infinity: 'That queer quantity 'infinity' is the very mischief, and no rational physicist should have anything to do with it. Perhaps that is why mathematicians represent it by a sign like a love-knot.'

$$\infty$$

What Eddington calls love-knot is in fact a lazy 8; mathematicians call it the lemniscate. The symbol was introduced in 1655 by the English mathematician John Wallis (1616-1703). He used it as shorthand, which is still used in calculus, for the phrase 'becoming large and positive'.

The young man in this classic limerick was so entangled in the infinity's love-knot that he decided to find the square root of infinity to impress his girlfriend:

There was a young man from Trinity
  Who solved the square root of
    infinity.
While counting the digits,
  He was seized by the fidgets,
Dropped science, and took up
    divinity.

Centuries ago Zeno was also seized by infinite fidgets when he discovered his famous paradoxes (see p. 18). And don't bother solving the square of infinity.

Here are some strange properties of infinity ($n$ is an ordinary number):

- $n + \infty = \infty$
- $n - \infty = -\infty$
- $n \times \infty = \infty$ (if $n$ is not equal to 0; if $n$ is negative, $n \times \infty = -\infty$)
- $\infty/n = \infty$ (or $-\infty$ if $n$ is negative)
- $n/\infty = 0$
- $n/0 = \infty$ (if $n$ is not negative or equal to 0). For practical purposes it is not a 'legal' fraction.
- $\infty + \infty = \infty$
- $\infty \times \infty = \infty$
- $\infty - \infty$, $0 \times \infty$, $\infty/\infty$ all give 'undefined answer'. These operations are not allowed.

14

## Zero

# Infinity's twin

We never buy zero things, yet zero is indispensable.

'The point about zero is that we do not need to use it in the operations of daily life,' says British philosopher and mathematician Alfred North Whitehead (1861-1947). 'No one goes out to buy zero fish.'

Yet our lives would be different without zero. There are two uses of zero: as a number itself meaning 'nothing', and as an empty placeholder in our place-value number system. For example, the number 500 implies that only the hundreds column contains any value and the two places to the right of 5 are 'empty'.

In the fourth century BC Babylonians used a placeholder in their sexagesimal (base-60) counting system to mark an absent unit. But this placeholder did not signify 'the number zero' and did not have the meaning of 'nothing' as in '5 − 5 = 0'. The zero, as we know it to be

today, first appeared in AD 458 in a Hindu cosmology text, but indirect evidence shows that it may have been in use as early as 200 BC. 'There was neither no-existence then; there was neither the realm of space nor the sky which is beyond? What stirred? Where?' says the *Rig Veda*, an ancient Hindu scripture. In the eighth century AD the Hindu place-value system of numerals, now known as the decimal or base-10 system, spread to Arabic countries. In 1202 the Italian mathematician Leonardo Fibonacci introduced the concept of the decimal system to Europe (see p. 45).

'Zero is powerful because it is infinity's twin,' notes Charles Seife in his book *Zero: The Biography of a Dangerous Idea* (2000), 'they are equal and opposite, yin and yang. They are equally paradoxical.' Like infinity (see p. 13), zero has many unusual properties:

- Zero is considered an even number, and is the basis of the definition of even numbers.
- Any non-zero number multiplied by zero is zero ($n \times 0 = 0$).
- A number divided by zero equals infinity ($n/0 = \infty$). Therefore, zero cannot be in the denominator (bottom number) of a fraction; it is not a 'legal' fraction.
- Zero can be in the numerator (top number) of a fraction ($0/n$). This fraction, which is a 'legal' fraction, is always equals to zero. This is a unique property of zero; this is equivalent to the statement that any non-zero number multiplied by zero is zero.
- Any number raised to the power of zero ($n^0$) is always equal to 1; zero raised to the power of zero ($0^0$) is usually taken to be equal to 1 also, except in abstract analytical mathematics.
- Zero divided by zero ($0/0$) also gives an 'undefined' answer. This operation is not allowed.
- When zero is added or subtracted from a number the answer is the original number ($n \pm 0 = n$).

We end this essay on zero — which by now you know is more than nothing — with a verse by the French poet Raymond Queneau (1903-76):

When One made love to Zero
  spheres embraced their arches
and prime numbers caught their
  breath...
— *Pounding the Pavements (1967)*

See also PRIME NUMBERS, p. 37.

16

# Pi

# An amazing ratio

Pi is one of the most important and ubiquitous numbers
in mathematics.

All circles are similar and the ratio of the circumference to the diameter is always the same number. This ratio is known as pi ($\pi$). Like the square root of 2 (see p. 88) pi is an irrational number. It takes infinite digits to express it as a decimal number. It is impossible to find the exact value of pi; however, the value can be calculated to a very high degree of accuracy.

Pi's story is probably as old as the story of mathematics. The Babylonians were the first to find the value of pi as 3. A passage in the Old Testament shows that the Hebrews, like Babylonians, also accepted pi as 3. From an ancient papyrus written in c. 1700 BC by the Egyptian scribe Ahmes (see p. 30), we learn that Egyptian mathematicians used 3.16 as the value of pi (the correct value is 3.14159...). In the third century BC Archimedes approximated this value to 3.14. A century later, the Greek astronomer Ptolemy improved the value to 3.1416, a remarkable achievement.

Pi was introduced in to Europe in the sixteenth century. In 1650 the English mathematician John Wallis (1616-1703) worked out unlimited series for the calculation of the value of pi. This opened a new crazy field in mathematics — calculation of the value of pi to an unlimited decimal place. The craze still continues, but the work is now done by computers. The latest record for computing the value is to 1,351,100,000,000 decimal places. This was achieved in 2004 by a Tokyo University supercomputer.

The symbol $\pi$ was introduced by the Swiss mathematical Leonhard Euler (see p. 71). He took the first letter for the Greek word for perimeter to represent this amazing ratio.

See also SQUARING THE CIRCLE, p. 27;
BUFFON'S NEEDLE PROBLEM, p. 77.

17

# Motion is an illusion

Zeno's four paradoxes on motion had a profound influence on the development of mathematics and philosophy. Their validity is still debated 2,500 years after they were first propounded.

Very little is known about Zeno (*c*. 490-*c*. 425 BC) who was born in Elea, Lucania (now southern Italy). All we know about him comes from Parmenides (*c*. 370 BC), one of the dialogues of the Greek philosopher Plato (*c*. 429-*c*. 347 BC). Parmenides was a student and friend of Zeno. Plato mentions that Zeno wrote forty paradoxes. In his great book, *Physics* (*c*. 350 BC), Aristotle describes Zeno's four paradoxes on motion, all of which seemed to prove that motion is an illusion. They are:

### The dichotomy

There is no motion because that which is moved must arrive at the middle of its course before it arrives at the end. Let's take an example to explain this paradox. To cover a distance of one metre point, you must first reach the ½ metre, before that ¼ metre, before that ⅛, and so on forever.

### Achilles and the tortoise

This most famous of Zeno's paradoxes says that the faster of two runners can never overtake the slower, if the slower is given any start at all. Thus, Achilles, a hero of Trojan War reputed to be the fastest runner ever known, will never catch a slow tortoise that started first. Achilles must first reach the point which the tortoise has just left, so that the tortoise must always be some distance ahead. Let's say the tortoise has a 100-metre head start. When Achilles, who is 10 times faster than the tortoise, has run 100 metres the tortoise will have crawled 10 metres, and so will be 10 metres in front. And so it goes infinitely. As Achilles has infinite gaps to traverse, he can never catch the tortoise.

Zeno was so perplexed by the concept of infinity (see p.13) that he thought that motion was impossible. He assumed that space and time are infinitely divisible, that is, the sum of an infinite number of numbers is always infinite. The paradox was resolved 2,000 years later by the Scottish mathematician James Gregory (1638-75) who showed that an infinite number of numbers can add to a finite number.

**The arrow**
This paradox says that a flying arrow is at rest: at every instant of its flight the arrow occupies a space just its own size, meaning at every instant of its flight it is at rest. The paradox is based on the assumption that time is made up of discrete instants which are indivisible. Therefore, we can't have a speed at an instant (speed is distance travelled divided by elapsed time, but there's no elapsed time at an instant). Albert Einstein's (1879-1955) discovery that time itself varies, depending on speed, led to the modern concept of instantaneous speed, which allows us to calculate how fast an object is travelling at a given instant, thus resolving the paradox.

**Stadium**
This paradox concerns two rows of equal bodies moving past each other in the stadium at equal speeds in opposite directions, one row starting from the end of the stadium, the other from the middle. The paradox assumes that a body takes an equal time to pass with equal speed a body in motion and a body of equal size at rest, but it's not true.

See also NINE-ROOMS PARADOX, p. 99.

# Axioms, proofs and theorems

The geometry described by Euclid in his book *Elements* and based on five axioms is known as Euclidean geometry.

L ittle is known of Euclid's life. He lived around 300 BC and taught at the Great Library at Alexandria in Egypt, the impressive library of antiquity with more than 400,000 volumes.

According to an anecdote, when a student innocently asked what profit he might gain from studying geometry, Euclid ordered a slave to give him a coin so that he could make a profit from studying geometry.

Euclid is chiefly remembered now for *Elements*, a book that presents a complete system of elementary geometry. This book influenced mathematicians and scientists for nearly 2,000 years.

Even Isaac Newton (1642-1727), in his majestic *Philosophiae Naturalis Principia Mathematica*, expressed his thoughts in the language of Euclidean geometry. When Newton, who had lent a friend copy of *Elements*, enquired what progress he had made and how he liked it, the friend asked what use and benefit in life that kind of study would be to him. 'Upon which Sir Isaac was very merry,' as a contemporary writer records Newton's amusement. No, unlike Euclid, Newton didn't ask his house servant to give a coin to his friend.

Axioms are self-evident truths that don't require proof. Five axioms or postulates form the basis of Euclidean geometry:

1. A straight line can be drawn between any two points.

2. A straight line can be extended indefinitely.

3. A circle can be drawn with any given centre and radius.

4. All right angles are equal.

5. If two lines are drawn which intersect a third in such a way that the sum of the inner angles on one side is less than two right angles, then the two lines must inevitably meet; that is, they cannot be parallel to each other. (This postulate is complicated and Euclid himself was reluctant to use it.)

A proof is a series of statements in which each statement is derived from a previously proved statement or an axiom. The final statement is known as a theorem. A proof leads from assumptions to conclusions, or axioms to theorems. Sometimes QED (abbreviation for the Latin *quod erat demonstrandum*, meaning 'which was to be shown') is written to denote the end of a proof.

Let's prove the theorem 'in an isosceles triangle the angles at the base are equal' in Euclidean style ('isosceles' means 'having two sides of the same length').

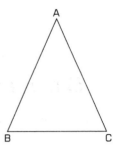

ABC is an isosceles triangle in which AB = AC.

Let's imagine this triangle as two triangles: the triangles ABC and ACB.

Since AB = AC, and AC = AB, then the two sides BA, AC are equal to two sides CA and AB respectively, and ∠BAC = ∠CAB, because it is the same angle.

∠ABC (opposite side AC) = ∠ACB (opposite the equal side AB).

Therefore, angles opposite the equal sides are equal.

Therefore, in an isosceles triangle the angles at the base are equal.

QED

See also ANALYTICAL GEOMETRY, p. 50.

# Outsmarting the donkey

An angle inscribed in a circle is a right angle.

Thales (*c.* 624-*c.* 545 BC), one of the so-called 'Seven Wise Men' of antiquity is considered the founder of Greek science, mathematics and philosophy.

His scientific ideas were derived from observed facts. He offered rational rather than supernatural explanations. In mathematics, he is believed to be the first to prove that an angle inscribed in a circle is a right angle. There is no record of his proof, but a proof appears in Euclid's *Elements* (see p.20), which goes something like this:

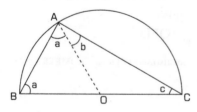

Draw a semicircle with centre O and diameter BC and choose any point A on the semicircle.

We have to prove that ∠BAC is a right angle, Draw line OA. In triangle AOB, OB and OA are the same length as they are radii of the same circle. So, triangle AOB is an isosceles triangle and in an isosceles triangle the base angles are equal (see p. 21; Thales was also the first to prove this result). Therefore, ∠ABO = ∠BAO.

Similarly, in triangle AOC, OA and OC have the same length (radii of the same circle) and so ∠OAC = ∠OCA.

From the large triangle BAC we see that ∠ABC + ∠ACB + ∠BAC = 2 right angles (again, Thales was the first to prove that the sum of the angles of a triangle equals two right angles). Or,

$$2 \text{ right angles} = \angle ABC + \angle ACB + \angle BAC$$
$$= a + b + (a + b)$$
$$= 2a + 2b$$
$$= 2(a + b)$$

$$1 \text{ right angle} = \tfrac{1}{2} [2 \text{ right angles}]$$
$$= \tfrac{1}{2} [2(a + b)]$$
$$= a + b$$
$$= \angle BAC$$

QED

Thales also accurately predicted the solar eclipse in 585 BC; and while travelling in Egypt he astounded the Egyptians by measuring the height of a pyramid by means of shadows.

His interest in astronomy is supported by this famous story. One night he was gazing at the sky as he walked and fell into a ditch. A girl lifted him out and remarked sarcastically: 'Here's a man who wants to study stars, but cannot see what lies at his feet.'

According to another famous story, a farmer's donkey routinely used to carry heavy bags of salt to market. One day the donkey fell into a stream, thereby dissolving much of the salt and making the burden lighter. The smart donkey learned the trick of rolling over wherever he crossed the stream. The farmer approached Thales for advice who told him to load the donkey with sponges on the next trip to the market.

Pythagoras' theorem

# A walk on a chequered floor

Pythagoras' theorem is the most famous theorem in history.

Legend has it that the Greek mathematician Pythagoras (*c*. 508-*c*. 500 BC) discovered the relationship between the sides of a right angled-triangle — the square on the hypotenuse is the sum of the squares on the other two sides — when he was walking on the chequered floor of a temple in Egypt.

The floor of the temple had alternately coloured squares. The shadows of the pillars were falling obliquely across these squares. The shadow and the squares suggested different geometrical patterns. Pythagoras' interest in geometry led him to study these patterns from different angles and then to the discovery of the proof of the theorem that now bears his name.

The theorem has numerous practical applications. It is indispensable to surveyors for finding heights, distances and areas. About 367 different

proofs of the theorem have been supplied since the time of Pythagoras. One of the most famous proofs was given by Euclid (see p. 20) and you have probably encountered it in your geometry class. The following proofs is one of the trickiest:

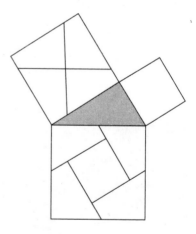

In this picture one square has been dissected into four parts. These four parts and the smaller square can be fitted into the larger square, proving the famous theorem. If you want to try it out yourself, read on: On a piece of paper, draw squares on the sides of a right-angled triangle (as shown in the diagram on p. 24). Mark the centre of the upper square. Rule two lines through the centre, at right angles to each other and with one line parallel to the triangle's hypotenuse. Cut out the four parts and the smaller square. Now try to fit these five pieces into the larger square. It's tricky, if you do not know the answer shown in the diagram.

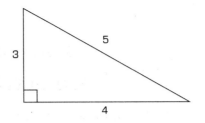

This proof was discovered in 1830 by Henry Perigal (1801-98), a London stockbroker and amateur mathematician. He was so pleased with his discovery that he had the diagram printed on his business card. The diagram, somewhat faded, can still be seen on his tombstone in the church in the little sleepy town of Wennington in Essex, near London.

They may not know it, but builders and gardeners use Pythagoras' theorem every day when they measure out a '3-4-5 triangle' to make a right-angled corner:

By Pythagoras' theorem,
$$3^2 + 4^2 = 5^2$$
$$9 + 16 = 25$$
So the angle is exactly a right angle.

Duplicating the Cube

# The oracle speaks

Duplicating the cube is a classical problem of antiquity.

The problem appears in a Greek legend which tells how in 428 BC the Athenians, suffering under a plague, sought, guidance from the oracle at Delos as to avert the plague.

In ancient Greece the oracle at Delos was considered second only to the famous oracle of Delphi. The oracle advised to double the size of the cubical altar to Apollo. The Athenians dutifully doubled the linear dimensions — length, width and height — of the altar. But the gods were not pleased and the terrifying disease continued to ravage Athens. The oracle had in fact advised to double the volume of the cube; the Athenians, however, had increased the volume eightfold. This is the origin of the problem of constructing a cube twice the volume of a given cube.

Let's consider a cube with the length of sides $a$. Its volume is $a^3$. To duplicate this cube we will have to construct a cube whose volume is $2a^3$, or its sides are the cube root of $2a^3$. It is impossible to construct a cube of these dimensions with ruler and compass and the ancient Greeks failed to find a solution for the problem. The problem had to wait for the mathematics of the nineteenth century for a solution.

There is a similar construction problem from antiquity: trisecting an angle. Again, this problem cannot be solved by means of ruler and compass. The third similar problem is squaring the circle (see p. 27). In mathematics literature this 'impossible trio' is referred to as the three classical problems of antiquity.

# Impossible!

Squaring the circle is one of the greatest problems in classical geometry.

Pi (see p. 17) is an irrational number. This means that it could not be expressed as a fraction or terminating decimal or as an infinite recurring decimal.

The ancient Greeks were not aware of this fact. Almost every great Greek mathematician tried in vain to solve a problem which was, in fact, impossible.

The problem is to square a circle; that is, to draw a square equal in area to a given circle. The quest to find a solution continued into the eighteenth century. The Paris Academy received so many erroneous proofs that in 1775 it passed a resolution not to examine any proofs. The problem, at last, was 'solved' in 1882 when the German mathematician Ferdinand von Lindemann (1852-1939) proved unequivocally that squaring the circle was an impossibility.

Archimedes (c. 287-212 BC), the greatest scientist, mathematician and mechanical genius of antiquity, was the first to show that the problem is equivalent to finding the area of a right-angled triangle whose sides are equal respectively to the circumference of the circle and the radius of the circle. Half the ratio of these two lines is equal to pi.

See also DUPLICATING THE CUBE, p. 26; THE ARCHIMEDES PALIMPSEST, p. 28.

# Eureka!

The works of Archimedes were found buried within a medieval prayer book. Known as the Archimedes palimpsest, its secrets are now revealed.

The story of the Archimedes palimpsest begins in about 1229 in a Constantinople monastery.

When an Eastern Orthodox priest named Ioannes Myronas ran out of parchment, specially prepared and scraped animal skin, for a prayer book he was copying, he used the pages from five old manuscripts. He scrubbed the pages with natural acid and pumice stone, cut them into half, rotated them 90 degrees, folded them and wrote his prayers at right angles to the faint traces of the earlier handwriting. Such a recycled manuscript is known as a palimpsest (from the Greek *palimpsestos*, meaning 'again rubbed smooth').

The prayer book, almost intact, found its way to the Church of the Holy Sepulchre in Istanbul, where in 1906 it came to the attention of Johan Ludvig Heilberg, a philologist and professor of the history of mathematics at the University of Copenhagen. Squinting through a magnifying glass he could see some mathematical writings beneath the prayers inscribed by Myronas. He photographed pages for later study. He was shocked to find that it contained some of the books of Archimedes, which had never been discovered before. A few months later the manuscript went missing, until it appeared at a Christie's auction in New York in 1998. An anonymous bidder paid $2 million for the manuscript. The new owner, known only as 'Mr B', deposited the manuscript at The Walters Art Museum in Baltimore, Maryland, a few months later.

Using advanced imaging technology, scientists have now a clearer view of the hidden text, which includes the only known copies of *The Method of Mechanical Theorems, On Floating Bodies* and fragments of *The Stomachion* (a tangram-like puzzle, see p. 131). The museum curators have described their findings as 'Archimedes' brain on parchment'. The parchments deciphered so far reveal that he understood infinity (see p. 13) and could even operate with it. They also show how he developed his proofs and theorems, and suggest that he discovered combinatorics, an important technique in modern computing.

Today, Archimedes is mostly remembered for the tale of his running naked through the streets shouting: 'Eureka! Eureka!' King Hiero of Syracuse, suspecting that his goldsmith had adulterated his newly built gold crown with silver, asked Archimedes to find out the truth without damaging the crown. Archimedes discovered that the crown was adulterated, along with his famous scientific principle, at bath time. He noticed that — when getting into a tub full of water — the level of water rose as he got in.

Less well known is the story of Archimedes' tragic death. When the Roman general Marcellus captured Syracuse, a Greek city in Sicily, he gave strict orders that no harm was to come to Archimedes. But the orders never reached the detachment of Roman soldiers who found him in his backyard drawing some complicated geometrical figures on sand. Seeing the soldiers, Archimedes shouted: 'Do not touch my drawings!' One of the soldiers drove a spear through the body of the great thinker, when he could well have been contemplating something further for the benefit of humankind.

The Romans buried him with honours and veneration and marked his tomb by a sphere inscribed in a cylinder. He had asked that at his death his grave should be marked with this particular drawing, with an inscription showing that the volume of the sphere is exactly two-thirds of the volume of the circumscribed cylinder.

See also SQUARING THE CIRCLE, p. 27.

# From the time of pharaohs

The Rhind papyrus is one of the oldest known mathematical documents.

The Rhind papyrus is a papyrus scroll, about 5 metres (18 feet) long and 33 centimetres (13 inches) high. It was found in an ancient tomb in Thebes, Egypt, and was bought in 1858 by a Scottish antiquary Alexander Henry Rhind (1833-63).

The papyrus, which has been in the British Museum since 1864, is one of the two oldest mathematical documents in existence. The other is in Moscow.

Known as the Moscow papyrus (or the Golenischev papyrus after its former owner), it's the same length as the Rhind papyrus but is only about 7.5 centimetres (3 inches) wide. Though older than the Rhind papyrus, it's a collection of 25 Egyptian mathematics problems. The Rhind papyrus is a mathematical handbook and our main source of Egyptian mathematics.

The papyrus was compiled in about 1700 BC by a scribe named Ahmes. The modest scribe introduces his script by saying that he copied it from an earlier document compiled in the time of Amenemhet III (reigned 1842-1797 BC). Written in hieratic script (a simplified and abbreviated form of the hieroglyphic script), it contains some 85 problems showing the use of fractions, the solution of simple equations and progressions, and calculation of areas and volumes.

The papyrus has five problems on pyramids. Problem 56 says: 'If a pyramid is 250 cubit high and the length of its base is 360 cubit, what is its seked (or seqed)?' The seked of a pyramid is the inclination of any one of the four triangular faces to the horizontal plane of its base. In other words, it's the angle of the slope of a pyramid's face, which is in fact

A small section of the Rhind papyrus

How much grain is saved by the 7 houses' cats?' He points out the similarity between this ancient Egyptian puzzle and the eighteenth-century Mother Goose rhyme:

As I was going to St Ives
  I met a man with seven wives.
Every wife had seven sacks,
  Every sack had seven cats,
Every cat had seven kits.
  Kits, cats, sacks and wives,
How many were there going to St Ives?

its arctangent. Ahmes' answer corresponds to an angle of 54° 15' between the base and the face.

In *The World of Mathematics* (1956), the editor James R. Newman describes a problem in the Rhind papyrus which has been interpreted thus: 'In each of 7 houses are 7 cats; each cat kills 7 mice; each mouse would have eaten 7 ears of spelt; each ear of spelt would have produced 7 hekat of grain. Question:

Still struggling with the problem? The astonished man below wants to tell you that the answer is where he started counting up to 1 million. The correct answer can be found on page 167.

1,000,000 in the ancient Egyptian hieroglyphics

Platonic solids

# 'Let no one ignorant of geometry enter here'

Platonic solids are five regular polyhedrons first described by Plato.

A polyhedron is a solid whose faces are in the shape of polygons.

In a regular polyhedron all faces are identical. There are infinitely many types of polyhedrons possible, but there are only five regular polyhedrons. They are, from left to right in the diagram below, the tetrahedron (a pyramid with triangular faces); the cube; the octahedron (an 8-sided solid with triangular faces); the dodecahedron (a 12-sided figure with pentagonal faces); and the icosahedron (a 20-sided figure with triangular faces).

These five solids were first described by the Greek philosopher Plato in his book *Timaeus* (c. 360 BC). He also showed how they could be constructed by putting triangles, squares and pentagons together to form their faces.

The ancient Greeks believed in four 'elements' — earth, air, fire and water — out of which the whole world was created. Plato associated the cube with earth, the octahedron with air, the tetrahedron with fire and the icosahedron with water; he used the dodecahedron for the universe as a whole. Plato was a great believer in geometry and the words 'Let no one ignorant of geometry enter here' were inscribed over the door of his Academy in Athens.

## Conic sections

# Curves of our life

Circles, ellipses, parabolas and hyperbolas can be generated
by running a plane through a cone.

The Greek mathematician Apollonius of Perga (260-190 BC), known as the Great Geometer, described these conic sections in his book *Conics*. He also coined the terms ellipse, parabola and hyperbola. *Conics*, written in the formal language of Euclidean geometry (see p. 20), originally had eight books but only the first four have survived.

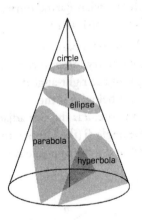

The circle has only one
centre and a constant radius

and that is why all circles are the 'same shape'. The ellipse has no radius and no centre as such. It has two perpendicular axes and two points called focus. Mathematically, a parabola is the set of all points that are equidistant from a point and a line. The point is called the focus, and the line directrix. The hyperbola is an infinite curve.

Circular ripples form when a stone is dropped into a pond, or when light waves are diffracted as they pass through a small hole. The ellipse, parabola and hyperbola all occur in nature. The orbits of planets are elliptical. When you throw a ball in the air, its path is a parabola. When two stones are thrown in a pool of water, the concentric circles of ripples intersect in hyperbolas.

See also DESCARTES' CIRCLE
THEOREM, p. 51.

33

# Yardstick to the heavens

Trigonometry, at its simplest level, is the study of how the sides and angles of a triangle are related to each other.

The Greek astronomer Hipparchus (*c.* 190-*c.* 120 BC), now known as 'the father of trigonometry', was the greatest stargazer of antiquity. For the first time in Greek astronomy, he applied a yardstick to the heavens. He used circular instruments divided into degrees and fitted with simple sighting devices for his observations.

From his observatory at the island of Rhodes he drew up a list of 1080 stars, arranged them in 48 constellations and classified them according to their brightness. Thus he created the first known star catalogue. The ancient Greeks believed that the stars were fixed on a gigantic sphere and only the planets moved on the sphere. Therefore, to understand these positions on the sphere they used spherical geometry, the geometry of the two-dimensional surface of a sphere. Hipparchus was the first to devise a trigonometric table of ratios for such two-dimensional figures.

Hipparchus did not invent the word 'trigonometry'. The word, however, comes from the Greek words *trigonon* and *-metria*, meaning 'triangle' and 'measurer' respectively. It was introduced in 1595 by the German astronomer and mathematician Bartholomaeus Pitiscus (1561-1613).

Now some basics of trigonometry (often nicknamed 'trig'): In the right-angled triangle below, $h$ is the hypotenuse, $a$ is the side adjacent to the angle $\theta$ (the Greek letter theta) and $o$ the opposite side.

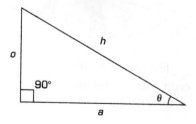

There are six basic functions that are used to interpret the measurement of angles and sides:

$$\sin \theta = o/h$$
$$\cos \theta = a/h$$
$$\tan \theta = \sin \theta/\cos \theta = o/a$$
$$\csc \text{ (or cosec) } \theta = 1/\sin \theta = h/o$$
$$\sec \theta = 1/\cos \theta = h/a$$
$$\cot \theta = 1/\tan \theta = a/o$$

The full names of these functions are sine (sin), cosine (cos), tangent (tan), cosecant (csc or cosec), secant (sec) and cotangent (cot). Equipped with this knowledge of trigonometry, you should now be able to solve this problem posed by the French novelist Gustave Flaubert (1821-80), of *Madame Bovary* (1857) fame:

Since you are now studying geometry and trigonometry, I will give you a problem. A ship sails the ocean. It left Boston with a cargo of wool. It grosses 200 tons. It is bound for Le Havre. The mainmast is broken, the cabin boy is on deck, there are 12 passengers aboard, the wind is blowing East-North-East, the clock points to a quarter past three in the afternoon. It is the month of May. How old is the captain?

— *from a letter written to his sister Carolyn in 1843*

Don't try too hard.

# Algorithm

# A series of steps

An algorithm is a step-by-step procedure to perform a specific task.

The eminent Greek mathematician Euclid (see p. 20) gave us one of the first algorithms when he solved the problem of the greatest common divisor (GCD) of two whole numbers; that is, the largest number that divides both numbers with no remainder.

Euclid's algorithm (in modern notation): if $a$ and $b > 0$, and $r$ the remainder after dividing $a$ by $b$, then GCD $(a, b)$ = GCD $(b, r)$. Repeated use of this algorithm gives two smaller numbers for which finding GCD is much easier. For example, to find the GCD of numbers 206 (that is, $a$) and 40 (that is, $b$), the first step is to divide 206 by 40 and note the remainder (6):

GCD (206, 40) = GCD (40, 6) Then divide 40 by 6, to find the new remainder (4):

GCD (40, 6) = GCD (6, 4) and so on: GCD (6, 4) = GCD (4, 2) GCD (4, 2) = (2, 0) Therefore, the GCD of 206 and 40 = 2

Like Euclid, the ninth-century Arabian mathematician Muhammad ibn Musa al-Khwarizmi (who gave us the word 'algebra') also believed that any problem could be broken down into smaller parts that can be solved individually. When his mathematical works became known to European mathematicians, his Latinised name, Algorismus, became synonymous with the step-by-step art of calculating. It became algorithm in English. Algorithms are used extensively in computer programming. For example, to find out how many students in a class are older than 15, you might write this simple algorithm:

For all students in the database If age > 15 add one to counter Print counter

In 1937 the British mathematician Alan Turing gave algorithm a mathematically precise definition (see p. 118).

# The infinitude of primes

Prime numbers are the key to cryptic codes, which keep internet commerce secure.

Prime numbers are positive whole numbers (other than 1) that are divisible only by themselves and 1. The list starts with 2 and continues indefinitely:

2, 3, 5, 7, 11, 13, 17, 19, 23, 29, 31, 37, 41, 43, 47, 53, 59, 61, 67, 71, 73, 79, 83, 89, 97, 101, 103, 107, 109, 113, 127, 131, 137, 139, 149, 151, 157, 163, 167, 173, 179, 181, 191, 193, 197, 199, 211...

By using computers, mathematicians today have uncovered the first 1.5 billion prime numbers. The list doesn't follow any regular pattern; the numbers appear to be distributed at random. The list also shows that 2 is the only even prime number.

In his book *Elements*, Euclid (see p. 20) proves that there are infinitely many prime numbers. The proof is a mathematical classic — a superb model of reasoning. In modern notation the proof goes something like this: Euclid begins with a finite set of prime numbers, say $A$, $B$, $C \dots N$. Let's find a new prime number $P$ different from all these, $P = A \times B \times C \dots N + 1$. Clearly $P$ being 1 more than the product of all the prime numbers in the initial list, it doesn't equal any of them. Since $A$, $B$, $C \dots N$ constitute all prime numbers, $P$ can't be a prime number. Thus it must be divisible by at least one of finitely many prime numbers, say $N$. But when we divide $P$ by $N$ we get remainder 1. That's a contradiction, so our original assumption that there are finitely many prime numbers must be false. Therefore, there are infinitely many prime numbers.

See also THE SIEVE OF ERATOSTHENES, p. 38; MERSENNE PRIMES, p. 39.

# The sieve of Eratosthenes
# Draining the primes

The sieve of Eratosthenes is a simple ancient method for
finding prime numbers.

Eratosthenes (276-194 BC)
was the first to measure the
circumference of the Earth. We
remember him not only for this
astonishing achievement, but
also for his 'sieve'.

A versatile scholar — an
astronomer, mathematician,
geographer, historian, literary
critic and poet — he was born
in Cyrene (now Shahhat, Libya).
He was appointed the head of
the Great Library of Alexandria
in 236 BC. He became blind in
195 BC and died the following
year of voluntary starvation.

To find prime numbers, say
less than 100, by the method
of Eratosthenes, make a list of
all numbers. First, cross out 1,
because it is not a prime number.
Circle 2 and then cross out every
multiple of 2. Circle 3 and then
cross out every multiple of 3.
Continue the process until all the
numbers have either been circled
or crossed out. The numbers you
have circled are prime numbers.

| 1 | 2 | 3 | 4 | 5 | 6 | 7 | 8 | 9 | 10 |
|---|---|---|---|---|---|---|---|---|---|
| 11 | 12 | 13 | 14 | 15 | 16 | 17 | 18 | 19 | 20 |
| 21 | 22 | 23 | 24 | 25 | 26 | 27 | 28 | 29 | 30 |
| 31 | 32 | 33 | 34 | 35 | 36 | 37 | 38 | 39 | 40 |
| 41 | 42 | 43 | 44 | 45 | 46 | 47 | 48 | 49 | 50 |
| 51 | 52 | 53 | 54 | 55 | 56 | 57 | 58 | 59 | 60 |
| 61 | 62 | 63 | 64 | 65 | 66 | 67 | 68 | 69 | 70 |
| 71 | 72 | 73 | 74 | 75 | 76 | 77 | 78 | 79 | 80 |
| 81 | 82 | 83 | 84 | 85 | 86 | 87 | 88 | 89 | 90 |
| 91 | 92 | 93 | 94 | 95 | 96 | 97 | 98 | 99 | 100 |

See also PRIME NUMBERS, p. 37.

# A monk's gift

So far mathematicians have discovered only forty-four
Mersenne prime numbers.

The search for prime numbers has fascinated mathematicians since Euclid showed that number of primes is infinite (see p. 37).

In his book *Elements*, Euclid proposed an amazing theorem which, in modern notation, says: if $2^n - 1$ is prime for $n > 1$, then $n = 2^{n-1} (2^n - 1)$ is a perfect number (see p. 40). Mathematicians soon discovered that $2^n - 1$ could only be prime for values of $n$ that were prime.

In 1644 Marin Mersenne (1588-1648), a French monk, gave a new life to this formula when he said in his book *Cogitata Physica-Mathematica* that he had found the values of $n$ which would give a prime number. He believed that these special primes were 2, 3, 5, 7, 13, 17, 19, 31, 67, 127 and 257. Later mathematicians found many errors in his list. The correct list is: 2, 3, 5, 7, 13, 17, 19, 31, 61, 89, 107 and 127. Now numbers of the form $2^n - 1$ are known as Mersenne numbers and those that result in prime numbers are called Mersenne primes.

The 44th prime, discovered in 2006, is an extremely large number. It has 9,808,358 digits. The search of other Mersenne primes continues. The Great Internet Mersenne Prime Search (GIMPS) Project (at www. mersenne.org) is leading this search. The project has found the last ten Mersenne primes.

## Perfect numbers

# 'Six is a number perfect in itself'

A perfect number is a number equal to its factors
not including the number itself.

The following four perfect numbers have been known from ancient times and they were also known to Pythagoreans who considered that the numbers ruled the universe (see p. 144):

$$6 = 1 + 2 + 3$$
$$28 = 1 + 2 + 4 + 7 + 14$$
$$496 = 1 + 2 + 4 + 8 + 16$$
$$+ 31 + 62 + 124 + 248$$
$$8128 = 1 + 2 + 4 + 8 + 16 + 32$$
$$+ 64 + 127 + 254 + 508$$
$$+ 1016 + 2032 + 4064$$

Numbers 6 and 28 were known in biblical times and it was believed that they reflected the structure of the universe: the world was created in six days, and the moon orbits the earth every 28 days. St Augustine (354-430) writes in his famous book *The City of God*: 'Six is a number perfect in itself, and not because God created all things in six days; rather, the converse is true. God created all things in six days because the number is perfect. And it would remain perfect even if the work of the six days did not exist.'

Euclid (see p. 39) showed that $2^{n-1} (2^n - 1)$ is a perfect number whenever $(2^n - 1)$ is a prime numbers. Euler (see p. 71) proved that Euclid's formula includes all even perfect numbers. We still do not know whether there are any odd perfect numbers.

See also MERSENNE PRIMES, p. 39.

# Hypatia

# The poster girl

Hypatia was the first notable woman in mathematics.

Hypatia (*c.* 370-415) was the daughter of Theon of Alexandria, a mathematician and astronomer at the Great Library of Alexandria in Egypt.

In 400 she became the head of Neo-Platonist school of philosophy at Alexandria. She was also an outstanding mathematician and inventor. Only the titles of her mathematical works have survived, but sources describe her as a mathematician who surpassed her famous father's talents. She wrote commentaries on the *Arithmetica* of Diophantus, the *Conics* of Apollonius and the *Almagest* of Ptolemy. She invented, among other things, a plane astrolabe to measure the position of stars, planets and the sun.

Hypatia was a pagan in an increasingly Christian city. One dark night in 415, on the way home from the Library, she was dragged off her chariot by a mob of extremist Christians, stripped naked, hacked to death, and her remains burned.

The English novelist Charles Kingsley (best known for *The Water Babies*) presented a romantic picture of her life in his novel, *Hypatia — or New Foes with an Old Face* (1853). This and other works have perpetuated the legend that Hypatia was not only intellectual but also beautiful. In the twentieth century the life and death of beautiful and brilliant Hypatia was romanticised by feminists and she became the poster girl of modern mathematics and science. Hypatia's death marked the beginning of the decline of the Library as the major centre of ancient learning and also the end of the golden age of Greek mathematics and science. In 641 the Arab armies of the Caliph of Baghdad not only razed the Library buildings, but burned the books to heat the public baths.

# Running back again

Palindromic numbers are numbers that read the same backwards as forwards.

The word *palindrome* is from the Greek *palindromos*, meaning 'running back again'.

The idea of palindrome also applies to words, phrases and verses; for example, 'radar', 'madam, I'm Adam'. The Greek poet Sotades, who lived in the third century BC, was the first to create the word palindromes. The earliest reference to a palindromic number, 12345654321, appears in a ninth-century AD Hindu mathematics text.

Here's an interesting number game: (1) take any whole number; (2) reverse its digits; (3) add the result to the original number. If the answer is not a palindrome, repeat steps 1, 2 and 3. You will always end up with a palindrome.

For example:

Step 1    73
Step 2 +  37
Step 3 =  110

The answer is not a palindrome. Let's repeat steps 1, 2 and 3:
110 + 011 = 121.

A palindrome!

Most numbers require fewer than five iterations, except for the number 196. This is the only number less than 10,000 that has not yet produced a palindrome by this process.

Mathematicians have used computers to repeat the process for this stubborn number nearly 725 million times, but have failed to find a palindrome.

# A simple rule

The rule of three is an ancient method of solving proportions.

Multiplication is vexation;
  Division's twice as bad;
The rule of three perplexes me,
  And fractions drive me mad.

This old nursery rhyme suggests that the rule of three is perplexing, but it's a very simple rule.

The rule first appeared in the works of the seventh-century Indian mathematician Brahmagupta: 'In the rule of three, argument, fruit and requisition are the names of the terms. The first and last terms must be similar. Requisition multiplied by fruit, and then divided by argument, is the produce.' Or, produce = requisition × fruit/argument.

We can easily understand Brahmagupta, when we apply algebra. If we know three numbers $a$, $b$ and $c$ and want to find $d$ and the numbers are in proportion $a:b = c:d$, then $a/b = c/d$ or $d = cb/a$.

In old days every school child learned this rule. Even Abraham Lincoln learned it in his one-room schoolhouse. Lewis Carroll (see p. 96) writes about it in his 'Mad Gardener's Song':

He thought he saw a Garden-Door
  That opened with a key:
He looked again, and found it was
  A double Rule of Three:
'And all its mystery,' he said,
  'Is clear as day to me!'

# An astonishing number

The golden ratio is a mathematical relationship that has
fascinated mathematicians, philosophers and artists
since ancient Greece.

In his book *Elements*, Euclid (see p. 20) shows how to divide a straight line AB into two by a point C so that the ratio of the longer segment (AC) to the shorter one (CB) is exactly the ratio of the entire line (AB) to the longer segment (AC). Irrespective of the length of the line, the ratio is always equal to 1.61803398887... which is an irrational number (see p. 88).

This ratio is now known as the golden ratio or divine ratio and is denoted by the Greek letter phi ($\Phi$). Phi is the only positive number that becomes its own reciprocal by subtracting 1; that is, $1/\Phi = \Phi - 1$ $= 0.61803398887...$

A          C     B

Ancient Greeks used phi extensively in art and architecture as they considered it pleasing to the eye. The exterior dimensions of the Parthenon in Athens, built in about 440 BC, form a perfect golden rectangle (a rectangle whose sides are in golden ratio).

Curiously, phi also appears in the natural world: in mollusc shells, sunflower florets, in certain crystals and shape of galaxies containing billions of stars. For example, the seeds on a sunflower are arranged in two sets of spirals. The ratio of the number of seeds in the two spirals is phi. When a falcon dives towards its prey, it swoops in along a path that is mathematically related to phi.

See also FIBONACCI SEQUENCE, p. 45

## Fibonacci sequence

# 'The Da Vinci Code'

The Fibonacci sequence is a series of numbers in which each successive term is the sum of the preceding two:
1, 1, 2, 3, 5, 8, 13, 21, 34, 55, 89, 144...

The Fibonacci sequence has many interesting mathematical properties. If you divide each number into the one that follows it (1/1, 2/1, 3/2, 5/3, 8/5...) the answer approaches the number 1.6181... This number is known as the golden ratio (see p. 44). If you square any Fibonacci number, the answer will differ by no more than 1 from the product of two adjacent Fibonacci numbers.

Fibonacci numbers are named after the Italian mathematician Leonardo Fibonacci (*c.* 1170-*c.* 1250). During his travels in North Africa Fibonacci learned of the decimal system that had evolved in India and had been taken up by the Arabs.

Upon his return to his home town Pisa he published a book *Liber Abaci* (1202) in which he introduced to Europe the Arabic numerals we use today.

'These are the nine figures of the Indians: 9 8 7 6 5 4 3 2 1. With these nine figures, and with this sign 0 which in Arabic is called *zephirum*, any number can be written, as will be demonstrated,' he wrote in his book.

Fibonacci is now best known for the simple series of numbers which comes from the answer of a puzzle posed by him: 'Beginning with a single pair of rabbits, if every month each productive pair bears a new pair, which becomes productive when they are one month old, how many pair of rabbits will there be in one year?'

The first eight Fibonacci numbers appear as one of the clues left by murdered museum curator Jacque Saunière in Dan Brown's bestselling novel *The Da Vinci Code* (2003).

Cycloid

# The Helen of geometry

The cycloid is considered the most beautiful curve in
geometry; that's why it's named after the legendary beauty.

There is probably another reason for this name: like Helen of Troy it provoked many quarrels among the mathematicians in the seventeenth century.

The French named it *la pomme de discorde* ('the apple of discord'). To us the cycloid is a beautifully proportioned curve, but to mathematicians it is the curve described by a point on the edge of a circle rolling along a straight line, also called the locus of the point.

The cycloid was discovered in 1501 by the French mathematician Charles Bouvelles (1471-1553). Like many mathematicians before him he was trying to solve the impossible problem of squaring a circle (see p. 24). It was named in 1599 by Galileo. Since then it has been studied by many great mathematicians, including Fermat, Descartes, Newton, the Bernoullis and Pascal, who appear in this book.

The cycloid has many curious properties: the path of a pendulum is an inverted cycloid. Galileo suggested the use of cycloid arches for bridges as they would be stronger to any other curves. Christopher Wren (1632-1723), the London architect who designed St Paul's Cathedral,

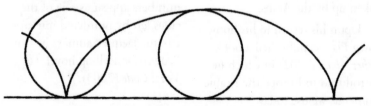

Every point on the edge of a rolling wheel traces a cycloid

calculated that the length of such arches is exactly four times the generating circle.

The cycloid also leads to an interesting brainteaser: At any instant on a moving train, are there parts of the wheels that move backwards — not forward? The following diagram shows the cycloid traced by every point on the rim of a moving train wheel. This cycloid is called a curate cycloid: cycloid generated by a point inside the rolling circle. It shows that there are points on the wheel that are moving backwards as the train moves forwards.

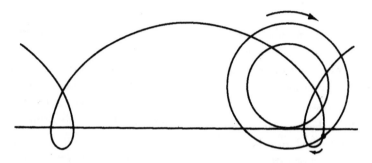

The cycloid traced by the rim of a moving train wheel shows that there are points on the wheel that are always moving backwards

# Logarithms
# A useful concept

Logarithms are used in many areas of science and engineering, especially when dealing with quantities that vary over a large range.

The logarithm of a number is the value of the power to which a base must be raised to get the given number.

For example, the logarithm of 100 to the base-10 is 2, or $\log_{10} 100 = 2$. This is because $10_{10} = 100$. Logarithms to the base-10 are called common logarithms and to the base-$e$ are called natural logarithms (for the meaning of $e$ see p. 70). The logarithm of a number $x$ in base-$e$ is written as $\log_e x$ or $\ln x$.

The most common properties of logarithms (for all positive bases) are:

- $\log_a 1 = 0$ (because $a^0 = 1$)
- $\log_a a = 1$ (because $a^1 = a$)
- $\log_a a^x = x$ (because $a^x = a^x$)

Logarithms were invented by the Scottish mathematician John Napier (1550-1617). In 1594 it occurred to him that all numbers could be written in exponential form; that is, 4 can be written as 22 and 5 as 2 with some fractional power between 2 and 3. It took him another twenty years to work out the detailed rules and tables of logarithms, which he published in 1614 in *Mirifici logarithmorum canonis descriptio* (*Description of the Wonderful Canon of Logarithms*).

In the book's introduction Napier noted that he hoped that his logarithms would save much time and free mathematicians from the slippery errors of calculations. He was right. Logarithm tables — and the slide rule invented in 1621 by the English mathematician William Oughtred (1575-1660) which was also based on logarithms — remained in common use for more than three centuries until hand-held calculators became popular.

48

## Kepler's conjecture

# The proof is in the packing

### What is the best way to pack spheres as densely as possible?

In the 1590s, while stocking his ship for an expedition, the English nobleman and adventurer Sir Walter Raleigh asked his assistant Thomas Harriet if there was a quick way of estimating the number of cannonballs in a given stack.

A few years later Harriet presented the problem to the German astronomer and mathematician Johannes Kepler (1571-1630), now famous for his three laws of planetary motion.

After experimenting with different ways of stacking spheres, Kepler stated in 1611 what he thought was the obvious solution: an arrangement known to all greengrocers but called the face-centred cubic lattice by mathematicians. In this arrangement, you place, say 100 oranges, in a flat layer of 10 × 10, then fit another layer into the interstices between the oranges in the first layer, and so on until the pile forms a pyramid. In such an arrangement, Kepler calculated, 74 per cent of the volume is taken up by the spheres, and 26 per cent by the spaces between the spheres. But Kepler didn't provide a proof.

The search for the proof for Kepler's conjecture dogged mathematicians for centuries, from classic greats Isaac Newton and Carl Friedrich Gauss to modern masters David Hilbert and Buckminster Fuller. In 1998 Thomas Hales of the University of Michigan stunned the mathematics world when he announced that he has found the proof (which consisted of 250 pages of arguments and 3 gigabytes of files). In 2003 the prestigious journal *Annals of Mathematics* accepted the proof as definitive. Some mathematicians do not like computer proofs of problems. They like the elegance of equations. We may have to wait another 400 years for an elegant proof.

# Algebra meets geometry

Analytical geometry has been called the greatest single step
ever made in the progress of the exact sciences.

The French philosopher and mathematician René Descartes (1596-1650) believed that the Euclidean geometry (see p. 20) 'exercises the understanding only on condition of greatly fatiguing the imagination'.

To make things simple, he decided to handle lines and plane figures on a graph. This idea gave birth to a new geometry now known as analytical (or coordinate or Cartesian) geometry.

The graph is made by arbitrarily choosing two lines of references (usually horizontal and vertical lines) that are at right angles to each other. These lines of references are normally referred to as $x$-and $y$-axes. Any point on this graph can be described by two numbers $x$ and $y$ — called the coordinates of the point — $x$ representing the distance along the $x$-axis and $y$ along the $y$-axis. This graph is a two-dimensional Cartesian space. A set of $x$-, $y$- and $z$-axes that are right angles to each other defines a surface in a three-dimensional Cartesian space.

The French writer Voltaire (1694-1778) described analytical geometry as 'the method of giving algebraic equations to curves'. For example, the equation $(x − 2)^2 + (y − 5)^2 = 36$ or $6^2$ represents a circle whose centre is at the point $x = 2, y = 5$ and whose radius is 6 units. The equation for a circle with its centre at the intersection of the $x$- and $y$-axes always follows the form $x^2 + y^2 = r^2$ where $r$ is the radius.

## Descartes' circle theorem

# Four kissing circles

*The theorem describes an elegant relationship between the radii of four mutually tangential circles.*

I n 1643 Descartes (see p. 50) developed a formula relating the curvature of four circles, each of which touches all of the other three. The curvature (or bend) of a circle is defined as $1/r$ where $r$ is the radius of the circle.

For four circles with curvatures $a$, $b$, $c$ and $d$, the formula specifies that $a^2 + b^2 + c^2 + d^2 = \frac{1}{2}(a + b + c + d)^2$. This formula also applies to three touching circles nested within a fourth circle.

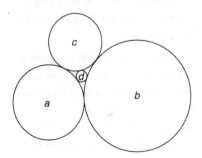

When in 1936, Frederick Soddy (1877-1956), the English chemist who was awarded the 1921 Nobel Prize for chemistry, rediscovered the theorem he penned a poem which was published in the journal *Nature* (20 June 1936). An excerpt:

Four circles to the kissing come,
The smaller are the benter.
The bend is just the inverse of
The distance from the centre.
Though their intrigue left Euclid dumb
There's now no need for rule of thumb.
Since zero bend's a dead straight line,
And concave bends have minus sign,
The sum of the squares of all four bends
Is half the square of their sum.

Apollonius was the first to study tangent circle (see p. 33).

## The Gregorian calendar

# 'Give us back the eleven days'

The calendar we have today is the Gregorian calendar which replaced the old Julian calendar.

Our present calendar year started in 45 BC when Julius Caesar introduced a calendar based on the solar year. This solar calendar replaced the old lunar one in which each month starts at the new moon and lasts about 29.5 days.

But Caesar's astronomers had not been accurate: they estimated the length of the year 11 minutes and 14 seconds longer than the true solar year of 365 days 5 hours 48 minutes 46 seconds, the time it takes the earth to make its orbit around the sun.

By the middle of the sixteenth century, the Roman inaccuracy had piled up ten extra days. In 1582 Pope Gregory XIII produced a solution: he ordered that ten days should be dropped out of the calendar for that year; 5 October was followed by 15 October. He also established that leap days to be inserted after 28 February every four years, except those century years which are not divisible by 400 (1900 was not a leap year, but 2000 was). The Gregorian calendar was readily accepted by all European countries except Sweden, Russia and England.

In 1752 Lord Chesterfield told English Parliament to reform the calendar: 'It was not... very honourable to England to remain in gross and unavowed error.' By that time the accumulated error was eleven days. He proposed that 2 September should be followed by 14 September.

There was feverish opposition to the innovation. Many people genuinely believed that their lives had been cut short by eleven days. Lord Chesterfield was harassed through the streets by crowds hooting and shouting: 'Give us back the eleven days we have been robbed of!' Bankers and landlords were reluctant to lose eleven days' interest and rent. The financial year end, which for centuries had been 25 March, was changed to 5 April. This is still the end of financial year in Britain.

The British — followed by the Swedes in 1753 — resigned themselves to the loss, but the Russians held out until 1918. As a result, the Bolshevik coup of 7 November 1917, according to the Gregorian calendar, is known as the October Revolution (23 October in the Julian calendar).

The Gregorian calendar is sufficiently close to the true solar year and it would take 3,322 years to accumulate an error of one day. While we're waiting for that extra leap day, we're going to get many leap seconds. But leap day and leap second are two absolutely different things.

One rotation of the earth — spinning of the earth on its axis as opposed to its orbit around the sun — takes exactly 24 hours and is called mean solar day. The earth's rotation is gradually slowing down because of the braking action of the tides. The average deceleration is roughly 1.4 milliseconds per day per century. A leap second is added to the time every two civil years to keep atomic clocks synchronised with the earth's rotation. The last leap second was added on 31 December 2008. Don't worry! The earth won't stop rotating after a few millenniums. Leap second is not a measure of the rate at which the earth is slowing. It is the correction between two time systems, one measured by the spin of the earth and the other by atomic clocks.

# Thinking in letters

Music has been called pure algebra of enchantment, but algebra may not seem to you pure music of enchantment.

'Perhaps the subject will appear rather difficult, inasmuch as it is not yet familiar (beginners are, as a rule, too ready to despair of success); but you, with the impulse of your enthusiasm and the benefit of my teaching, will find it easy to master; for eagerness to learn, when seconded by instruction, ensures rapid progress.' So writes Diophantus in the dedication of his book, *Arithmetica*, to his friend Dionysius.

Diophantus, a Greek mathematician who lived in Alexandria, Egypt, in the third century, is considered the founder of algebra, and *Arithmetica* one of the most influential books in the history of mathematics. Diophantus did not introduce today's algebraic notation, but he was the first to use symbols for the unknown quantities.

The use of letters as symbols representing numbers was introduced by François Vieta (1540-1603), a French mathematician. Another French mathematician René Descartes (1596-1650) decided that letters at the beginning of the alphabet, *a*, *b* and *c*, would be used for known numbers and those at the end of the alphabet, *x*, *y* and *z*, for the unknowns.

The plus and minus signs (+ and −) were first used in a book printed in Germany in 1489. However, the signs had been used earlier by dockworkers on sacks of grain to indicate that they were heavier or lighter than a standard weight. The multiplication sign (×) was first used in 1631 by the English mathematician William Oughtred (1575-1660). The division sign (÷) first appeared in an algebra book by the

Swiss mathematician Johann Rahn (1622-76). The Welsh mathematician Robert Recorde (1510-58) invented the equals sign (=). 'To avoid the tedious repetition of the words "is equal to",' he wrote in a book printed in 1557, 'I shall write as often as needed a pair of lines, like this: =, for no other two things could be more equal.' The greater-than and less-than symbols (> and <) first appeared in a book by the British mathematician Thomas Harriot (1560-1621) which was printed in 1631, ten years after his death.

Two word 'algebra' comes from the Arabic word *al-jabr*, meaning 'the reunion of broken parts', which appears in the title of a book, *Kitab al-jabr w'al-muqabala*, written by the ninth-century Arabian mathematician Muhammad ibn Musa al-Khwarizmi.

Algebra is 'easy to master' if you have the 'eagerness to learn' as promised by the founder himself, whether you agree or not with the opinion of American poet and author Oliver Wendell Holmes (1809-94) on the relative merits of arithmetic and algebra: 'One of the many ways of classifying minds is under the heads of arithmetical and algebraical intellects. All economical and practical wisdom is an extension of the following arithmetical formula: $2 + 2 = 4$.

Every philosophical proposition has the more general character of the expression $a + b = c$. We are mere operatives, empirics, and egotists until we learn to think in letters instead of figures.'

# Fundamental laws of numbers
# The traffic rules of algebra

These fundamental laws govern the order in which we perform operations in algebra.

**Commutative laws of addition and multiplication**
When we add or multiply, the order of numbers in which the numbers are added or multiplied does not affect the result:

$$a + b = b \times a$$
$$ab = ba$$

Changing the order of numbers is called 'commuting'. The commutative law does not work for either subtraction or division. The order of numbers will affect the result.

**Associative laws of addition and multiplication**
Associative law says that the grouping of terms in sum or product does not matter. This law allows you to move parentheses as long as the numbers do not move:

$$a + (b + c) = (a + b) + c$$
$$ab(c) = (ab)c$$

Associate law works only when we add or multiply; it does not work when we subtract or divide.

**Distributive law**
This law says that when the sum of two numbers is multiplied by a third number the result is the same as that obtained by multiplying each of the first two numbers, in turn, by the third number and then adding them. Put simply, the law allows a product of sums to be rewritten as a sum of products:

$$a(b + c) = ab + ac$$

The examples given above are for two or three elements, but the commutative, associative and distributive laws are valid for any number of elements. These laws, of course, are also valid in ordinary arithmetic.

## Identity law
This law concerns 0 and 1 only. It says that 0 has no effect on addition, and 1 has no effect on multiplication.

## Inverse law
This law says that $-a$ is the additive inverse of $a$; and $a^{-1}$ is the multiplication inverse of $a$ (when $a$ is not equal to 0).

This means:
$$a + (-b) = a - b$$
$$ab^{-1} = a/b$$

All these laws have been known to mathematicians for a long time, but they were summarised in the above form by various German and British mathematicians in 1830s.

# Speaking algebraically

Brackets help simplify algebraic operations.

O nce discussing his fellow American writers Cornelius Mathews and William Ellery Channing, Edgar Allen Poe (1809-49) remarked: 'To speak algebraically, Mr M is execrable, but MR C is $(x + 1)$-ecrable.'

The master of mystery and macabre surely knew how to disparage fellow writers algebraically — and use brackets for additional effect.

We use brackets in algebra to show that some operations need to be done on more than one term. For example, if you want to multiply $2x + 4y - 3$ by 5, you can either write:

$$5 \times 2x + 5 \times 4y - 5 \times 3$$

which looks messy, or you can do it more elegantly by using brackets:

$$5(2x + 4y - 3)$$

Brackets show that each expression inside the brackets needs to be multiplied by 5. Most people find a minus sign outside a bracket confusing. For example, $x - (y + z)$ is the same as $x - y - z$ and $x - (y - z)$ is the same as $x - y + z$. Here the rule is very simple: if there is a minus sign outside the brackets, signs of all expressions inside the brackets are reversed when the brackets are removed:

$$5x - (2x + 4y - 3)$$
$$= 5x - 2x - 4y + 3$$

But if there is a plus sign outside the brackets, the signs inside the brackets are not changed when the brackets are removed:

$$5x + (2x + 4y - 3)$$
$$= 5x + 2x + 4y - 3$$

## Factors

# Winnie the Pooh's disappointment

A factor of a whole number is a smaller whole number that divides into the number without a remainder.

Suddenly Christopher Robin began to tell Pooh about some of the things: People called Kings and Queens and something called Factors... and then, as Pooh seemed disappointed, he added quickly, 'but it's grander than Factors.'

— A.A. Milne, *The House at Pooh Corner* (1928)

Indeed, factors are not that interesting — and grander. Here are some facts about factors that Christopher Robin didn't teach Pooh.

The integer (whole number) 1 is a factor of all positive integers, and every positive integer is a factor of itself. A prime factor is a factor that is a prime number (see p. 37). The number that is a factor of two numbers is a common factor of those two numbers; for example, 9 is a factor of 18 and 54, so 9 is a common factor of 18 and 54. The highest common factor (HCF) of 18 and 54 is 18. The smaller factors of 18 and 54 are 3, 6 and 9.

The lowest common multiple (LCM) of 18 and 54 is 3 as this is the smallest number that is the multiple of 18 and 54. There is a difference between the terms factor and multiple. We obtain multiple of a number by dividing that number by 1, 2, 3... in turn.

When we factorise we express a number as the product of some of its factors; for example:

$$12 = 6 \times 2 = 4 \times 3 = 2 \times 2 \times 3$$

# Think of powers and roots

Two opposite mathematical processes — power and
root — relate indices and surds.

Yet what are all such gaieties to me
Whose thoughts are full of indices
and surds?

— Lewis Carroll

In the numbers 23 and $a^n$, 3
and $n$ are the indices (singular:
index) or the powers. The
following are the laws of indices:

- *Multiplication:* The indices are
added; for example,
$a^m \times a^n = a^{m+n}$
- *Division:* The indices are
subtracted; for example,
$a^m \div a^n = a^{m-n}$
- *Power:* The indices are
multiplied: for example,
$(a^m)^n = a^{mn}$

- Negative indices become
positive; for example,
$a^{-m} = 1/a^m$

Surds are square roots (or cube
roots, etc.) of numbers which
cannot be reduced to a whole
number; for example, $\sqrt{2}$, $\sqrt{5}$.
The following are the general
rules for simplifying surds:

- $\sqrt{ab} = \sqrt{a} \times \sqrt{b}$
- $\sqrt{a} \times \sqrt{a} = a$

Now like Lewis Carroll (see
p. 96) your thoughts can be full
of indices and surds.

# A slippery concept

An average is a number that represents a group of numbers.

Comparing groups of numbers is tricky and therefore we compare averages. But some mathematicians think that averages are more likely to hide than disclose important facts.

K. C. Cole (*The Universe and the Teacup*, 1997), goes even further and says that averages are 'about the slipperiest mathematical concept ever to slide into popular conscious.' In his classic *Facts from Figures* (1951), M. J. Moroney quotes from the satirical magazine *Punch*:

The figure of 2.2 children per adult female was felt to be in some respects absurd, and a Royal Commission suggested that the middle classes be paid money to increase the average to a rounder and more convenient number.

Mathematicians express averages — 'a meagre piece of information', according to Francis Galton (*Natural Inheritance*, 1889) — in three different ways: mean, median and mode. The easiest way to find 'average' is calculate the arithmetic mean: add all numbers in the group and divide by the number or numbers in the group. In geometric mean all the numbers in the group are multiplied by each other and finding the $n$th root of the product, where $n$ stands for how many numbers there are in the group. For example, geometric mean of 2, 4, 8 is the cube root of $2 \times 4 \times 8$ or 64, which is 4. The arithmetic mean of 2, 4, 8, on the other hand, is $(2 + 4 + 8)/3 = 14/3 = 4.666...$

Median is the value of the middle number of a group of numbers. If the list contains an even number or numbers, the average of the two middle numbers is taken. Mode is the number that occurs most often in a group.

# Solved at last

Fermat's theorem baffled even the greatest of mathematicians for more than 350 years until it was finally solved in 1993.

Pierre de Fermat (1601-65), a French lawyer and amateur mathematician, had been reading his copy of the classic text *Arithmetica* by Diophantus (see p. 54) when he came across the equation $x^2 + y^2 = z^2$. He immediately realised that the equation has an infinite number of solutions.

It was Fermat's habit to scribble brief marginal notes in his copy. He wrote: 'There are no whole number solutions of the equation $x^n + y^n = z^n$ for $n$ greater than 2. I have discovered a truly marvellous proof of this theorem, which this margin is too narrow to contain.' This was Fermat's last theorem, which he discovered in year 1637. 'Fermat was a mathematician of the first rank,' notes E. T. Bell in his classic biographies of mathematicians *Men of Mathematics* (1937), 'a man of unimpeachable honesty, and an arithmetician without a superior in history.'

Andrew Wiles, a professor of mathematics at Princeton University, finally solved the theorem in 1993. When he was a school student in Britain, Wiles saw the theorem in a maths book in his public library. 'It looked so simple, and yet all the great mathematicians in history couldn't solve it,' he recalls. 'Here was a problem, that I, a ten-year-old, could understand and I knew from that moment that I would never let it go. I had to solve it.' And he did it, but it took him seven years of dedicated work. The final proof is 130 pages long.

## Binomial theorem
# 'A lot o' news'

The binomial theorem was Newton's first great discovery.

I'm very well acquainted, too, with
  matters mathematical,
I understand equations, both the
  simple and quadratical,
About binomial theorem I'm teeming
  with a lot o' news,
With many cheerful facts about the
  squares on the hypotenuse.

Here's the news about the binomial theorem Major-General Stanley is teeming with in Gilbert and Sullivan's opera *The Pirates of Penzance* (1879).

A binomial is any two numbers connected by the plus or minus sign, for example, $(a + b)$. The binomial theorem deals with expanding expressions of the form $(a + b)^n$ for various values of $n$ such as:

$$(a + b)^2 = a^2 + 2ab + b^2$$
$$(a + b)^3 = a^3 + 3a^2b + 3ab^2 + b^3$$
and so on.

Isaac Newton (1642-1727) did not discover the binomial expansion. It was known to thirteenth-century Chinese mathematician Yang Hui as well as seventeenth-century European mathematicians, including Blaise Pascal (1623-62) who showed that binomial expansion can be obtained by the array now known as Pascal's triangle (see p. 64).

Newton, however, discovered the binomial theorem which can be used to expand binomials to any given power without direct multiplication. The theorem works for negative as well as fractional values of $n$, for example, $-3$ or $\frac{1}{2}$. The discovery was made in 1665, when he was twenty-two years old, a few months before he received his Bachelor of Arts degree from Trinity College, Cambridge University. It is said that if Newton had discovered nothing else except the binomial theorem, he would still be remembered as a great mathematician.

## Pascal's triangle

# An amazing pattern of numbers

Pascal's triangle is a triangular pattern of numbers with numerous interesting properties.

```
              1
            1   1
          1   2   1
        1   3   3   1
      1   4   6   4   1
    1   5  10  10   5   1
  1   6  15  20  15   6   1
        and so on
```

After the first two rows, each number in the body of the triangle is the sum of two numbers in the row above to the left and to the right. Thus the next row would be: 1, 7, 21, 35, 35, 21, 7, 1.

Although the triangle was known before the time of the French mathematician Blaise Pascal (1623-62), it is named Pascal's triangle because he used it ingeniously to obtain binomial coefficients (see p. 63). The numbers in each row of the triangle are the coefficients in the expansion of $(a + b)^n$. For example, if $n = 3$, $(a + b)^3 = a^3 + 3a^2b + 3ab^2 + b^3$. Coefficients 1, 3, 3, 1 are in the third row.

Pascal also used the triangle in his theory of probability (see p. 75). For example, in how many different ways can you pick up two marbles from a box containing five different-coloured marbles? The answer is 10 (or the probability is 1 to 10). This number is in the second place in the fifth row of the triangle (number 1 at the top is counted as 0 row).

Fibonacci numbers (see p. 45) can also be found in the triangle. They are harder to locate, but if you look at an angle you will find the sequence 1, 1, 2, 3, 5, 8, 13... (look for: 1, 1 + 1, 1 + 2, 1 + 3 + 1, 1 + 4 + 3, 1 + 5 + 6 + 1...)

# The bane of students

Calculus deals with variable quantities.

Calculus is the gateway to higher mathematics.

To some students it seems awesome and, unfortunately, it becomes a barrier. Mathematicians make it more intimidating when they talk about 'the calculus'. Even in everyday language, when people want to emphasise the subject, they say, for example, 'the calculus of the situation demands...' instead of simply saying 'the situation demands'. Calculus is not difficult to master, but it seems to have some kind of mysterious aura when students first encounter it. Mathematics literature abounds with 'calculus songs' written by those who hate — or love — calculus.

This excerpt from an old song by an unknown writer sums up the despair of many students after the first lesson of calculus:

O Lord, hear my anxious plea
  Calculus is killing me
I know not of 'dx' or 'dy'
  And probably won't until the day I die.
Please, Lord help me in this hour
  As I take my case to the highest power.

Calculus is the gift of two great minds: Newton, who needs no introduction, and the German mathematician and philosopher Gottfried Leibniz (1646-1716). In 1684 Leibniz published a paper with a rather long title, which translates as 'A new method for maxima and minima, as well as tangents, which is impeded neither by fractional or irrational quantities, and a remarkable type of calculus for this'. By 'calculus' he meant 'a set of rules'.

Newton invented calculus as early as 1665. He called it 'fluxions' which could also be used to find maxima and minima, as well as tangents, and which were not impeded by fractional or irrational quantities. But he did not publish anything until 1687.

The feud between Newton and Leibniz over which of them had first devised calculus is well recorded in the history of mathematics. The controversy continued for years, but it is now thought that each developed it independently. However, the terminology and notation of calculus as we know it today is due to Leibniz. For example, Leibniz's symbols $\int$ (the elongated s) for summation and $d$ for derivatives are still used today.

Calculus is divided into differential and integral calculus. We don't know how much Major-General Stanley in Gilbert and Sullivan's comic opera *The Pirates of Penzance* (1879) knew about integral and differential calculus, but he sure alludes to them in 'The Major-General's Song' to impress the pirates:

I'm very good at integral and
    differential calculus,
  I know the scientific names of
    beings animalculous;
In short, in matters vegetable,
    animal, and mineral,
  I am the very model of a modern
    Major-General.

We doubt he knew that differential calculus deals with derivatives and integral calculus with integrals. A derivative of a function shows infinitesimal change in the function with one of its variables. The derivative of a function $y$ with respect to variable $x$ is usually written as $dy/dx$. The integral of the function $f(x)$ is the limit as $x$ approaches zero. It's written as $\int f(x)\, d(x)$.

Complex, isn't it?

At least, one good thing about calculus is that you always know what your limit is.

## Functions

# Love is a function of...

A function expresses dependence between two quantities.

To understand functions we must begin with ordered pairs. An ordered pair is a pair of numbers that have a significant order. The term is used in particular to denote a pair of Cartesian coordinates: $x$ and $y$ coordinates used on a grid to locate a point (see p. 50). These coordinates have a significant order: $x$ is the first number and $y$ the second number; thus (1, 2) does not equal (2, 1), for example, as they specify different points.

A relation, which is also known as relationship, is a set of ordered pairs $(x, y)$. The first elements in this ordered pair, the $x$-values, form the domain. The second elements, the $y$-values, form the range. Now, a function is a relation between two sets, the domain and the range. Or, a function is a set of ordered pairs in which each element of the domain has only one element associated with it in the range. For example, $f = \{(1, 2), (3, 5), (7, 9), (12, 16)\}$ is a function, with each set of number being an ordered pair. The domain is the set $\{1, 3, 7, 12\}$ and the range is the set $\{2, 5, 9, 16\}$. This function never has two ordered pairs with the same $x$ and different $y$ values.

Still confused? The following verse may enlighten you. It's by the Scottish physicist W. J. M. Rankine (1820-72) and appeared in his book *The Mathematician in Love* (1874), published after his death:

Let $x$ denote beauty, $y$ manners
    well-bred
  $z$ fortune (this last is essential),
Let $L$ stand for love — our
    philosopher said —
  Then $L$ is a function of $x$, $y$ and $z$
Of the kind that is known as
    potential.

# On the back of a tortoise

There is no magic in a magic square; it's simply an addition table.

I n a magic square, the numbers in all the rows, columns and diagonals of the matrix add up to the sum.

| 4 | 9 | 2 |
|---|---|---|
| 3 | 5 | 7 |
| 8 | 1 | 6 |

Magic squares have fascinated people for more than 4,000 years. The earliest record of a magic square appears about 2200 BC in China. The legend has it that Emperor Yu saw a magic square on the back of a tortoise on the bank of the Yellow River. The square, called *lo shu*, was considered to be magical as the sum of numbers in every row, in every column and every diagonal was the same number; that is, 15. The square the Emperor saw is shown here in modern representation.

In medieval times a variation of the magic square appeared. In this square cells are filled with $n$ numbers (or symbols) so that no row or column contains the same number twice and each number is used precisely $n$ times. The Swiss mathematician Leonhard Euler (see p. 71) was the first to study them systematically and call them Latin squares. The completed grid of the popular puzzle Sudoku is a Latin square (see p. 136).

# A theorem for the Bernoullis

The harmonic series is the sum of the reciprocals of
whole numbers.

In three generations, during the seventeenth and eighteenth centuries, the Bernoulli family of Switzerland produced eight mathematicians and scientists, several of them outstanding.

The Bernoulli's principle (the faster the flow the lower the pressure), known to science students, is named after Daniel (1700-82). Our story is about Johann (1677-1748), father of Daniel.

During Johann's time an infinite series, such as $1 + 2 + 3 + 4 + 5...$, was seen merely a sum of endless collection of terms and it was believed that such a series 'diverges to infinity'. Johann observed that in the harmonic series $1 + \frac{1}{2} + \frac{1}{3} + \frac{1}{4} + \frac{1}{5} +...$ the individual terms clearly get closer and closer to zero, yet their sum becomes infinite. This observation seemed so bizarre and counter-intuitive, but Johann proved that the harmonic series diverges to infinity. Although the theorem was proved by Johann, its proof appeared in *Treatise on Infinite Series* (1689), a book written by his elder brother Jakob (1654-1705).

William Dunham notes in his book *Journey Through Genius: The Great Theorems of Mathematics* (1990) that the proof moved Jakob to pen a mathematical verse:

As the infinite encloses an infinite
series
And in the unlimited limit appear,
So the soul of immensity dwells in
minutia
What joy to discern the minute in
infinity!
The vast to perceive in the small
what divinity!

*e*

# An irrational cousin of pi

e is the most important and ubiquitous number in
higher mathematics.

Some mathematicians say it is impossible to conceive of a universe in which *e* and π do not exist. Like π, *e* is an irrational number (see p. 88). Its decimal sequence goes on forever and does not repeat in any permanent pattern:

$$e = 2.71828182845904523536...$$

Martin Gardner, the well-known author of numerous books on science and mathematics, points out an interesting fact in the expansion of π and *e*:

Pi goes on and on and on...
And e is just as cursed.
I wonder: Which is larger
   When their digits are reversed?

Euler (see p. 71), as ubiquitous in mathematics as *e*, was the first to study and to use the symbol *e* in 1727 (the fact that it's the first letter of his name is merely a coincidence). In the classic *Mathematical Recreations and Essays* (1892), W. W. Rouse Ball writes about another coincidence involving *e*: 'If we compare two packs of cards (one of them having been well shuffled), card by card, what is the probability that we shall get right through the packs without finding a single coincidence?... the answer is $1/e$ (with an error of less than $10^{-69}$, for packs of 52 cards). Many people are prepared to bet that no coincidence will occur, so an unscrupulous gambler might profit by knowing that $e > 2$.'

See also LOGARITHMS, p. 48.

# Beautiful and profound

Many formulas and theorems bear the prolific Swiss mathematician Leonhard Euler's name. Here we present two absolutely mathematical formulas and one, well, absolutely tongue-in-cheek.

### The formula for polyhedrons
$$v + f - e = 2$$
In this formula $v$ is the number of vertices, $f$ the number of faces and $e$ the number of edges of a polyhedron. In other words, in any polyhedron the number of vertices and faces together is exactly two more than the number of edges. If you're not sure, a polyhedron is a solid figure, such as a cube or a pyramid, with many faces (see p. 32). Let's apply the formula to the cube:
$$8 + 6 - 12 = 2$$
to the tetrahedron
$$4 + 4 - 6 = 2$$
and to the buckyball (a newly discovered form of carbon in which atoms are arranged in tiny, hollow spheres shaped like soccer balls; its 32 faces include 12 pentagons and 20 hexagons):
$$60 + 32 - 90 = 2$$

### The formula that amazed Euler
$$e^{\pi i} + 1 = 0$$
This formula relates $e$, $\pi$, $i$, 1 and 0 — the five most important numbers in mathematics. Known as Euler's identity, it has been described as the most beautiful and profound statement in mathematics. Note that $e$ is the base of natural logarithms (see p. 48), $\pi$ an irrational number (see p. 88) and $i$ an imaginary number (see p. 89).

The following limerick by an unknown wit hints that even the great Euler was amazed by this relationship.

e raised to the $\pi$, times i,
  And plus 1 leaves you nought by a
  sigh.
This fact amazed Euler
  The genius toiler,
And still gives us pause, bye the bye.

(Note: Euler is pronounced 'oiler'.)

**The formula that proved that God exists** $a = b^n/n = x$

Euler (1707-83) has been described as the most prolific mathematician in history. In his later years Euler was invited by Catherine the Great to live in St Petersburg, Russia. When the French philosopher Denis Diderot (1713-84) visited her Court, Diderot tried to convert the courtiers to atheism. She asked Euler to silence Diderot. The British mathematician Augustus De Morgan (1806-71) tells what happened in his classic *Budget of Paradoxes* (1872):

Diderot was informed that a learned mathematician was in possession of an algebraical demonstration of the existence of God, and would give it before the Court, if he desired to hear it. Diderot gladly consented ... Euler advanced toward Diderot, and said gravely, and in a tone of perfect conviction: Sir, $a = b^n/n = x$, hence God exists; reply!

Diderot who had no knowledge of mathematics was speechless. He asked Catherine's permission to return at once to France.

# A collection of dots

In graph theory, a graph is a collection of dots that may or may not be connected to each other. These graphs bear no resemblance to graphs that chart data or represent equations.

More precisely, in graph theory, a graph consists of a set of vertices (dots) together with a set of edges (lines), each of which adjoins two vertices.

A graph typically represents a communication network or· relations between objects from a collection. The World Wide Web is an example of a graph in which the files are the vertices and the links from one file to another are the edges. The 'friendship' graph below shows relations among people at a party. If two persons are joined by lines, they are friends. No lines mean they are strangers.

In 1736 the Swiss mathematician Leonhard Euler (see p. 71) solved the famous — and real — problem of the seven bridges of Königsberg by graph theory. He is now considered the founder of graph theory and his solution the first theorem in graph theory. At that time Königsberg was a Prussian town on the river Pregel, which had seven bridges. The town people tried repeatedly, without ever succeeding, to cross all seven bridges without crossing a bridge twice and return to the starting point.

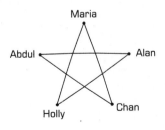

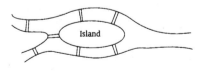

Euler simplified the problem by giving it a graphical representation. In his graph (see below), the banks and the island were represented by dots and the bridges by lines (B, C and D are banks, A the island and seven lines the bridges).

Euler showed that it was impossible to cross each bridge once and once only. To do so

an even number of lines must radiate from each dot, except for the two dots where the journey starts and finishes. But in the graph each dot A, B, C and D is linked to others by an odd number of lines. The problem could have been solved if one bridge were removed or added making the number of bridges even.

Two of the bridges and many other areas of Königsberg were destroyed by British bombers during the Second World War. The town is now part of Russia and is called Kaliningrad.

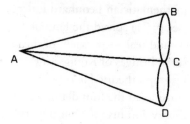

# Mathematics of chance

Probability is the mathematical concept that deals with the chances of an event happening.

The story of probability started in France in the seventeenth century when Chevalier de Méré, a nobleman and a gambler, wanted to know how to win in the two games of dice popular in the casinos of Europe at that time.

The first game consisted of rolling a die four times, and winning if a six would come at least once. The second game consisted of rolling two dice twenty-four times, and winning if a six would come at least once. The great gambler thought the chances of winning in both games would be the same. But when he continued losing his money on the second game, he asked his friend the mathematician Blaise Pascal (see p. 64) why he was having bad luck.

Pascal wrote to fellow mathematician Pierre de Fermat (see p. 62) and their correspondence gave birth to the theory of probability. 'The theory which originated in a gamblers' dispute is now at the base of many enterprises which we consider more important than gambling, including all kinds of insurance, mathematical statistics and their application, biology and educational measurements, and much of modern physics,' notes E. T. Bell, the eminent biographer of mathematicians.

We can find the probability of an event by simply dividing the number of ways the event can happen by the total number of possible outcomes:

$$\frac{\text{number of choices}}{\text{total number of possible outcomes}}$$

This rule can be applied to tossing coins, rolling dice, dealing cards or drawing lottery numbers. Let's take an example: What is the probability of drawing an ace of hearts from a well-shuffled pack of cards? There are four aces in a pack of 52 playing cards. The probability of drawing an ace is 4/52 or 1/13. The probability of drawing an ace of hearts is 1/52.

The following rules apply when we combine probabilities of two or more events.

**Mutually exclusive events:** A die has six faces, numbered 1, 2, 3, 4, 5 and 6. The probability that any one of these numbers comes is 1/6. What would be the probability of getting either a 3 or a 5? Because 3 and 5 cannot occur together, such an event is called a mutually exclusive event. In mutually exclusive events probability is calculated by adding individual probabilities, Therefore, the probability of getting either a 3 or a 5 is:

$$\frac{1}{6} + \frac{1}{6} = \frac{1}{3}$$

**Independent events:** When two dice are rolled separately, the second die does not take into account what the first die has done in order to decide what it will do. Such an event is called an independent event. In independent events probability is calculated by multiplying independent probabilities. Therefore, when two dice are rolled separately, the probability of getting a double 6 is:

$$\frac{1}{6} \times \frac{1}{6} = \frac{1}{36}$$

## Buffon's needle problem

# Drop the needle!

An early experiment that relates probability and π.

The calculation of the value of π has fascinated mathematicians for thousands of years (see p.17).

In 1777 the French naturalist and mathematician Georges-Louis Leclerc, Comte de Buffon (1707-88) tried a novel experiment to determine the value of pi. The experiment involved ruling equidistant parallel lines on a plane's horizontal surface. He then dropped a needle with a length equal to the distance between the lines repeatedly on the ruled surface. If the needle crossed or touched a line, the toss was considered favourable.

Buffon said that the probability of the needle crossing or touching the line is 2/π. If the needle is tossed at random $n$ times and it crosses or touches $c$ times, then $2n/c$ will approach π, if you keep on dropping the needle. The more drops, the more closely the result will approximate π.

In 1901 Mario Lazzarini, an Italian mathematician, tossed a needle randomly 3408 times and observed 1808 hits. From these figures he arrived at a value of 3.1415929 for π, which is correct to six decimal places. Subsequent similar experiments by other investigators have resulted in less accurate values of π. Some mathematicians now suspect that Lazzarini faked his results!

See also PROBABILITY THEORY, p. 75.

# Who wants to be a millionaire?

Every even number greater than 2 is the sum of two
prime numbers.

In 1742 the Russian mathematician Christian Goldbach (1690-1764) proposed a conjecture that every even number greater than 2 is the sum of two prime numbers: for example, $4 = 2 + 2$, $6 = 3 + 3$, $8 = 3 + 5$, $10 = 5 + 5$, and $3 + 7$, and $12 = 5 + 7$.

Remember that a prime number is a positive whole number that is divisible only by two numbers: itself and 1 (see p. 37). A conjecture is an unproven mathematical theorem. Goldbach's conjecture doesn't work for odd numbers; for example, 11 is not the sum of two prime numbers.

The conjecture remains one of the oldest unsolved problems in mathematics. No one has ever found an even number that can be expressed as the sum of two prime numbers. In recent years, mathematicians have used computers to test the conjecture against larger and larger numbers. So far they have verified the conjecture up to the number $6 \times 10^{16}$. But this doesn't mean the conjecture is right.

In 2000 the UK publishers of *Uncle Petros and Goldbach's Conjecture*, an engaging first novel by Greek author Apostolos Doxiadis, offered a prize of $1 million to anyone who proved the conjecture within two years of the publication of the novel. No one claimed the prize. Of course, the publicity the prize offer generated increased the sales of the book.

# De Moivre's theorem

# 'Sure as De Moivre'

De Moivre's theorem relates complex numbers
and trigonometry.

The theorem, familiar to students of trigonometry, was suggested by Abraham De Moivre in 1722.

It states that for any real number $x$ and any positive whole number $n$:

$$(cos\, x + i\, sin\, x)^n = cos\,(nx) + i\, sin\,(nx)$$

De Moivre was born in France in 1667. His family moved to England when he was a boy, where he spent the rest of his life. He studied mathematics on his own and became a teacher of mathematics. By chance he came across a copy of *Principia*, Newton's monumental work on gravitation, which made him interested in higher mathematics. He became quite an expert on *Principia* and corresponded with Newton on many topics.

There is an interesting story about De Moivre's death. A few weeks before his death on 27 November 1754, he declared that he would need twenty more minutes of sleep on each subsequent day. He died in his sleep after 72 days when the additional sleeping time had accumulated to 24 hours.

Mathematics did not make De Moivre rich and he lived an ordinary life; however, his famous theorem has made him immortal. Even the celebrated English poet Alexander Pope (1688-1744) paid tribute to him in his epic poem *Essay on Man* (1734):

Who made the spider parallels design,
Sure as De Moivre, without rule
or line?

79

## Carl Friedrich Gauss

# The prince of mathematicians

Gauss, with Archimedes and Newton, ranks as one of the greatest mathematicians of all time.

It has been said of the German mathematician Carl Friedrich Gauss (1777-1855) that almost everything which the mathematics of the nineteenth century has brought forth in the way of original scientific ideas is connected with the name of Gauss.

A versatile genius, among other things, Gauss formulated systematic and widely influential concepts and methods of number theory; discovered new methods for the calculation of the orbits of the planets, satellite, comets, etc.; investigated the passage of light through a system of lenses; invented a heliograph, the declination needle and a magnetometer; and worked with the German physicist Wilhem Weber (1804-91) on terrestrial magnetism and electromagnetism. The title *mathematicorum princeps* (the prince of mathematicians) bestowed upon him by his contemporaries is a fitting one.

Gauss was a *wunderkind* (wonder child) — a Mozart of mathematics. One Saturday in 1779, when he was not yet three, he watched his father making one of his weekly payrolls for the labourers under his charge. His father made a slip in his long computations, and he was astonished to hear the little boy say, 'Father, the calculation is wrong.' A check of the figures told his father that his *wunderkind* was right.

One day in his arithmetic class, when he was ten years old, the teacher asked the class to add together all the numbers from 1 to 100. The teacher had barely finished stating the problem, when Gauss, according to the custom of the class, put his slate on the teacher's table. 'There it lies,' the teacher exclaimed. He had given the question to keep students busy and did not know the answer himself. When he finished working the answer, he looked at Gauss' slate which had only one number written on it — 5050, the correct answer. (See below how Gauss worked out the answer.)

At age twenty-one, in 1798, he wrote his first masterpiece *'Arithmetical Researches'*, which founded modern number theory (see p. 82). Number theory, for him, was of paramount importance in mathematics.

'Mathematics,' he once asserted 'is the queen of the sciences, and the number theory is the queen of mathematics.' It is not just in number theory that Gauss has left his mark. 'He lives everywhere in mathematics,' remarks E. T. Bell, the historian of mathematics.

---

Write the numbers 1 to 100 twice like this:

$1 + 2 + 3 + 4 + 5 + 6 + 7 \ldots 94 + 95 + 96 + 97 + 98 + 99 + 100$

$100 + 99 + 98 + 97 + 96 + 95 + 94 \ldots 7 + 6 + 5 + 4 + 3 + 2 + 1$

Add the two lines, column by column:

$101 + 101 + 101 + 101 + 101 + 101 + 101 \ldots 101 + 101 + 101 + 101 + 101 + 101 + 101$

We have the number 101, 100 times, or

$101 \times 100 = 10100$

Therefore, the sum of numbers 1 to 100 will be half of 10100 or 5050. But Gauss didn't use this method to arrive at his answer. He used the formula $n(n + 1)/2$ in which $n$ can be any number, not only 100. We can arrive at this formula from the sum of numbers 1 to 100, or 1 to $n$, above in ascending and descending order. When we add the two lines, column by column, we get the number $n + 1$, $n$ times, which equals $n(n + 1)$, the half of which gives the answer. The only thing the wunderkind did was to find the value of 100 $(100 + 1)$ and halve it.

# Number theory
## Arithmetic for boffins

Number theory deals with properties of the positive integers
or whole numbers (1, 2, 3, 4, 5 ...).

Sometimes called 'higher arithmetic', number theory is one of the oldest and the largest branches of pure mathematics.

Number theory is complex and it is highly difficult to prove simple results. This aspect of number theory prompted Gauss (see. p. 80) to remark that 'it is just this which gives the higher arithmetic that magical charm which has made it the favourite science of the greatest mathematicians, not to mention, its inexhaustible wealth, wherein it so greatly surpasses other parts of mathematics'.

The 'inexhaustible wealth' Gauss mentions, includes in elementary number theory (other areas are outside the scope of this book) prime numbers (see p. 37), Fibonacci sequence (see p. 45), Fermat's last theorem (see p. 62) and Goldbach's conjecture (see p. 78).

Although modern number theory has its beginnings in the works of Gauss, many ancient Greek mathematicians, especially Diophantus (see p. 54), dealt with equations of the type $ax + by = 1$ and $x^n + y^n = z^n$ that allowed variables to be integers only.

## Set theory

# 'Too ready to despair of success'

Set theory is one of the greatest achievements of modern mathematics.

A set is a collection of distinct objects or things. Each item in a set is called an element or member. The element may be mathematical (3, 6, 9, 12... is the set of multiples of 3) or non-mathematical (John, Robin, Brian, all over 6 feet, are members of a set of 'tall people').

A set is usually denoted by a capital letter and its elements are listed between two braces { }; for example, E = {even numbers}. An empty or null set has no members (for example, the number of people who have visited Mars). Sets contained within sets are called subsets.

The German mathematician Georg Cantor (1845-1918) is the founder of the set theory. He was the first mathematician to say that infinity is not just an abstract concept, but an actual entity. Cantor was only twenty-nine when he published his first paper on infinite sets, in which he rejected the usual concept that the set of all integers or whole numbers (1, 2, 3 ...) is twice as big as the set of even numbers (2, 4, 6 ...). Cantor used the concept of pairability in place of our everyday concept of 'as many as'. He put these two sets into a one-to-one correspondence to show that the set of even numbers has an element to match every element of the set of all integers. This led him to realise that there were different 'orders' of infinity.

'Perhaps the subject will appear rather difficult, inasmuch as it is not yet familiar (beginners are, as a rule, too ready to despair of success).' When he wrote these words perhaps he was thinking of us mortals who are mortified of mathematics.

See also VENN DIAGRAMS, p. 85.

Lagrange's four-square theorem

# 'Before we create we must understand'

Every whole number is the sum of at most four squares.

In Diophantus's *Arithmetica* (see p. 54) appears a conjecture that every whole number is either a square itself or the sum of two, three or four squares.

No more than four squares are ever needed to express any number, no matter how big is the number. For example:

$$23 = 3^2 + 3^2 + 2^2 + 1^2$$
$$31 = 5^2 + 2^2 + 1^2 + 1^2$$
$$97 = 8^2 + 5^2 + 2^2 + 2^2$$

Diophantus didn't provide a proof for the conjecture. The first proof came in 1770 from the Italian-born French mathematician Joseph-Louis Lagrange (1736-1813). Because it has now been proved the conjecture is known as Lagrange's four-square theorem.

Lagrange made contributions in many areas of mathematics, including calculus, number theory, probability and algebra. He is one of the seventy-two scientists and other notable persons whose names are commemorated on the Eiffel Tower. The names appear in 60-centimeter letters on plaques that are permanently affixed to the sides of the tower just beneath the first platform with eighteen names per side. Lagrange once remarked: 'Before we take the sea we walk on land. Before we create we must understand.' How true!

# Immortal circles of Mr Venn

### A Venn diagram shows relationships between sets by overlapping circles.

The following Venn diagram shows two sets taken from the group of whole numbers 1 to 10: set A contains odd numbers 1, 3, 5, 7, 9 and set B comprises the numbers 6, 7, 8, 9, 10.

The numbers in the left circle are set A, the numbers in the right circle are set B. The central section contains numbers 7 and 9 which appear in both sets. The numbers 2 and 4 are outside the two circle as they are not in either set.

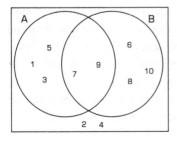

Similar diagrams were used by famous mathematicians Gottfried Leibniz (see p. 65) and Leonhard Euler (see p. 71) but they are now known as Venn diagrams after a little-known English logician John Venn (1834-1923) who extended the diagrams to visualise complex logical relationships. A single contribution has made Venn immortal. That's the quirk of history.

Venn diagrams can also be used to show the validity of a logical argument. For example, take the following line of reasoning: All albatrosses (A) are birds (B). No camels (C) are birds. Therefore, no camels (C) are albatrosses (A). The conclusion is evident from the following diagram.

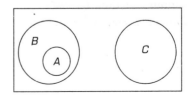

# Equations

## Knowledge in a capsule

An equation is a mathematical statement of equality.

Equations are symbolic representations of what we know of our physical world.

They are not ideas unto themselves; they are just the symbols that represent ideas. But they are an important part of our knowledge. Equations in pure mathematics do not apply to the real world, but in the physical world equations connect physical quantities.

The word equation comes from the Latin *aequare*, meaning 'make equal'. In an equation relationship between (unknown) variables is expressed using the equal sign '='. An equation may also contain (known) constants. The world's most famous equation, $E = mc^2$, shows that energy ($E$) and mass

($m$) are mutually convertible under certain conditions. In this equation $E$ and $m$ are variables and $c$ (the speed of light) is a constant. This equation is a consequence of Einstein's special theory of relativity (1905).

If you have equations, you are not alone. Stephen Hawking writes in *A Brief History of Time* (1988): 'Someone told me that each equation I included in the book would halve the sales. I therefore resolved not to have any equations at all. In the end, however, I did put in one equation, Einstein's most famous equation, $E = mc^2$. I hope that this will not scare off half of my potential readers.' It didn't. The book became the most popular science book of our time.

Fractions

# 'Five out of four people don't understand fractions'

Every year the *Washington Post* newspaper publishes a list of its favourite T-shirt slogans. This one made the 2001 list.

The word 'fraction' means a part of a whole.

In mathematics, a fraction is a number that is made up of the ratio of two whole numbers (integers). The top number is called the numerator, and the bottom number the denominator. The numerator and the denominator are separated by a '/' or '—'. For example, in the fraction $\frac{2}{3}$, 2 is the numerator and 3 the denominator. A fraction's numerator can be zero; such fractions always equal zero. But you cannot have zero as a denominator; the result is an undefined number (see p. 15).

Fractions observe some proprieties. If the numerator is smaller than the denominator (such as $\frac{2}{7}$), the fraction is called a proper fraction. It becomes an improper fraction if the numerator is larger than the denominator (such as $\frac{9}{4}$). A simple fraction in which the numerator and the denominator are integers is called a common or vulgar fraction (here 'vulgar' comes from the Latin *vulgaris*, 'the common people'). By this definition $\frac{2}{7}$ and $\frac{9}{4}$ both are vulgar fractions.

We are sure that if you have diligently followed this short lesson on fractions, you'll not be 'five out of four' people who don't understand fractions. And if you want to be philosophical about fractions, then listen to Harry Emerson Fosdick (1878-1969), an American preacher and author: '... when life ceases to be a fraction and becomes an integer.'

# Square root of 2

# An irrational number

A number is said to be square root of another number if,
when multiplied by itself, it gives the other number.

So 2 is square root of 4 because $2 \times 2 = 4$. But by this definition the square root of 2 doesn't exist. If we take any real number and square it we will never get 2. The square root of 2 as shown below is a decimal fraction which goes on forever and there is no pattern in its decimal sequence.

$$\sqrt{2} = 1.4142135623...$$

If we multiply the above number we will not get 2, but we will get closer and closer to 2 if we keep increasing the number of digits in the above decimal fraction. For this reason, square root of 2 is an irrational number. A number is called rational if it can be written as fraction $a/b$ where $a$ and $b$ both are whole numbers or integers. All rational numbers are real. Their decimal sequences do repeat. Decimal fractions whose sequences do not repeat are irrational.

Square root of 2 is the oldest known irrational number. The ancient Greeks discovered that the diagonal of a square whose sides are one unit long has a diagonal whose length cannot be rational. By Pythagoras' theorem, the length of the diagonal equals the square root of 2. So the square root of 2 is an irrational number.

Christoff Rudolff (1499-1545), a German mathematician, was the first to use square root symbol in his book, *Coss*, an arithmetic book printed in Strasburg in 1525. He probably derived the symbol from the letter $r$, the first letter of the Latin *radix*, meaning 'root'.

# Cardano's dilemma

Imaginary numbers are all non-zero multiples (which are real numbers) of the square root of −1.

Most numbers we use in our everyday life — positive numbers, negative numbers and zero — are real numbers.

When we square a positive or a negative number, the result is always a positive number. To square a number to get a negative number, mathematicians have invented imaginary numbers. For example, the number $\sqrt{-9}$ (square root of −9) does not exist, since no real number can have the negative number −9 as its square. The simplest imaginary number is the square root of −1; it has been given a special symbol $i$.

$$i = \sqrt{-1}$$

Imaginary numbers were first studied by the Italian physician and mathematician Girolamo Cardano (1501-76). In 1545 he published his greatest mathematical work *Ars magna* (*The Great Art*). In which he presented a formula for solving cubic equations. But he faced a problem when he tried to solve the cubic equation $x^3 - 15x - 4 = 0$. He knew that the equation had $x = 4$ as a solution, but his formula gave him an answer involving square root of a negative number. He therefore decided to accept the existence of such numbers, which are now known as imaginary numbers. Numbers that have a real and an imaginary part are called complex numbers. Complex numbers are used in formulas for alternating current (AC), airflow over aircraft wings, and many other engineering applications.

# Algebra of 0s and 1s

Boolean algebra is a set of rules, laws and theorems by which logical operations can be expressed and solved in a manner similar to ordinary algebra.

George Boole (1815-64), a self-taught British mathematician, is the founder of Boolean algebra. In 1854 he published his masterpiece *An Investigation into the Laws of Thought* in which he reduced logic to simple algebra.

'Boole's system of logic is but one of many proofs of genius and patience combined,' the notable British mathematician Augustus De Morgan (1806-71) commented on the book.

The importance of Boole's work was recognised when the first digital computers were built. They speak the language of 0s and 1s, a language invented by Boole. Boolean algebra's most important application is in computer circuits and internet search engines. All computer circuits function in one of two states: on or off, which can be represented by 1 or 0. These two digits are the building blocks of the binary code used to program instructions for computers. Incidentally, an unknown wit has pointed out that in the binary system we count on our fists instead of our fingers.

Three of the basic laws of Boolean algebra, associative laws, commutative laws and distributive laws, are the same as in ordinary algebra (see p. 54). Three important Boolean operations are called AND, OR and NOT. AND takes two input bits (1 or 0) in such a way that the output is 1 if all inputs are 1; it is 0 otherwise. For example, 1 AND 0 = 0, but 1 AND 1 = 1. OR combines two input bits in such a way that we get the output 1 whenever either, or both inputs are 1. For example, 0 OR 1 = 1, but 0 OR 0 = 0. NOT input is always the inverse of output. For example, 0 NOT = 1 and 1 NOT = 0.

## Mechanical computer

# 'Erroneous calculation'

Babbage's Analytical Engine was the forerunner of the modern digital computer.

Charles Babbage (1791-1871), an English mathematician, engineer and inventor, spent most of his life building machines that would perform mathematical operations and compute and print mathematical and navigational tables.

From 1819 to 1822 he worked on a machine which he called the Difference Engine. Made with toothed wheels on shafts that were turned by a crank, it was capable of calculating successive terms of the sequence $n^2 + n + 41$. He announced his invention in a paper 'Note on the application of machinery to the computation of astronomical and mathematical tables', which was read at a meeting of the Royal Astronomical Society in 1822. The Society awarded him a gold medal for this achievement.

He was always delighted to show his Difference Engine to his guests. Once a woman asked him: 'If you put in the wrong figure, will the right answer come out?' History does not record Babbage's response, but modern computers programmers are familiar with the phenomenon. They call it GIGO: garbage in, garbage out.

In 1824 Babbage turned his attention to a much grander machine, the Analytical Engine, capable of performing any mathematical operation. Although he prepared detailed drawings for thousands of parts, only a few parts were built. The level of technology at the time kept him from completing the machine which relied on precise mechanical parts and punched cards. The machine, like the modern computer, had a separate store (memory) for holding 1000 fifty-digit numbers and a 'mill' for working on them using tables from its own library (arithmetic unit), and a punched card system for specifying the sequence of instructions (input) and for obtaining results (output). Similar logical structure is used in modern computers.

After his death the British Association for the Advancement of Science established a committee to report on the feasibility of Babbage's design. The committee reported that 'its successful realisation might mark an epoch in the history of computation equally memorable with that of the introduction of logarithms'. What an understatement!

Babbage once sent a letter to the English poet Lord Alfred Tennyson (1809-92) about a couplet in '*The Vision of Sin*' (1869):

Every moment dies a man,
Every moment one is born.

He wrote: 'I need hardly point out to you that this calculation would tend to keep the sum total of the world's population in a state of perpetual equipoise, whereas it is a well-known fact that the said sum total is constantly on the increase. I would therefore take the liberty of suggesting that in the next edition of your excellent poem the erroneous calculation to which I refer should be corrected as follows:

Every minute dies a man,
And one and a sixteenth is born.

I may add that the exact figures are 1.167, but something must, of course, be conceded to the laws of metre.'

See also ADA LOVELACE, p. 93.

92

## Ada Lovelace

# 'Enchantress of Numbers'

*Lovelace effectively wrote the first computer program, but her program had no direct effect on the development of modern computer programming.*

Sir Alphabet Function, knight much
　　renown'd,
　Who had gained little credit on
　　classical ground,
Set out through the world his
　　fortune to try,
With nought in his pate but his *x*,
　*v* and *y*.

　　　　— Charles Babbage

Sir Alphabet Function was none other than Charles Babbage (see p. 91). In his later years he gave himself this moniker.

Babbage met Ada Lovelace (1815-52), daughter of the poet Lord Byron, when she was seventeen, and they began a life-long regular correspondence on mathematics and logic. In 1842 Luigi Menabrea, published a paper on Babbage's Analytical Engine. Babbage asked Lovelace, whom he used to call the 'Enchantress of Numbers', to translate the French edition of this paper into English. She not only translated the paper, but added a series of notes which

were three times the length of the original paper. In these notes, which are the source of her enduring fame as the world's first computer programmer, she outlined the fundamental concepts of computer programming and wrote instructions for programming the calculations of the Bernoulli numbers.

'The distinctive characteristic of the Analytical Engine, and that which has rendered it possible to endow the mechanism with such extensive faculties as bid fair to make this engine the executive right-hand of abstract algebra... We may say most aptly that the Analytical Engine weaves algebraical patterns just as the Jacquard loom weaves flowers and leaves,' she writes in the notes, *Observations on Mr Babbage's Analytical Engine*, which were published in 1843 under the pseudonym of A. A. L.

## Abel's impossibility theorem

# A jewel of mathematics

An extraordinary proof of an old problem by a 22-year-old
genius.

If you have studied mathematics at high school, you might have some idea of quadratic equations of the form $ax^2 + bx + c = 0$ in which $x$ is a variable and has two solutions or 'roots'. If $x$ is raised to the power 3, we get a cubic equation of the form $ax^3 + bx^2 + cx + d = 0$. Similarly, there are equations of higher degrees: quartic equations that involve $x^4$, quintic equations that involve $x^5$, and so on right up to $x^n$.

Mathematicians say that such equations are 'solvable in radicals', meaning any root, such as a square root for quadratic equations, a cube root for cubic equations, and so on. The roots of quadratic, cubic and quartic equations can be found by algebraic formulas which have been known for centuries, but mathematicians struggled for nearly three centuries to come up with a similar algebraic solution for quintic equations. In 1824 Niels Henrik Abel (1802-29)

proved that no radicals exist for quintic equations or equations of higher degrees. He proved the impossibility by the logical method known as *reductio ad absurdum* (Latin: 'by reducing to the absurd'). It's a method of proof in which you start by stating a proposition and then showing that it results in a contradiction. Abel assumed that the quintic is solvable and then showed that this assumption results in a logical contradiction.

Abel died when he was only twenty six, but in his very short life he made great contributions to mathematics. It is said that 'he has left mathematicians something to keep them busy for five hundred years'. In 2002 the Norwegian Academy of Science and Letters established the Abel Prize for outstanding work in mathematics. The annual prize is presented Nobel-style by the king of Norway.

See also GALOIS THEORY, p. 95.

## Galois theory

# A stroke of genius

Galois theory, most of which was feverishly scribbled by a 20-year-old genius the night before his death, has revolutionised algebra.

Abel showed that there is no formula that will work for all quintic equations and equations of higher order (see p. 94). However, some equations can be solved for radicals, but others cannot. How can we determine whether a quintic equation or an equation of higher order can be solved by a formula? A young French mathematician Évariste Galois (1811-32) sought to find the answer. In this process he turned algebra 'on its ears', remarks Mario Livio in *The Equation That Couldn't be Solved* (2005).

If we want to know whether an equation is solvable or not, we try to solve it. Galois rejected this time-honoured method. Instead he looked at the 'shapes' or algebraic symmetries of the equation to find an answer. He associated each equation with some kind of generic property — now known as the Galois group — and then used it to determine whether a given equation is solvable or not. This brilliant and complex theory laid the foundations of the group theory which has fundamental importance in all mathematics.

When he was twenty years old, Galois was challenged by the flancé of a girl he had fallen in love with. During the duel he received a pistol shot in the abdomen and died the next morning. During the last hours of his life he scribbled feverishly on the manuscript of his theory commenting on it, once breaking off to scribble in the margin *'Je n'ai pas le temps'* ('I have no time'), one of the most memorable quotes in the history of mathematics. 'What he wrote in those desperate hours before the dawn will keep generations of mathematicians busy for hundreds of years,' notes E. T. Bell, the eminent historian of mathematics.

# Alice's maths lessons

The immortal Alice books, *Alice's Adventures in Wonderland* and *Through the Looking Glass*, swarm with word plays and mathematical humour, jokes, riddles and puzzles.

Alice meets the Mock Turtle and the Gryphon and discusses school with them:

'And how many hours a day did you do lessons?' said Alice, in a hurry to change the subject.

'Ten hours the first day,' said the Mock Turtle: 'nine the next, and so on.'

'What a curious plan!' exclaimed Alice.

'That's the reason they're called lessons,' the Gryphon remarked: 'because they lessen from day to day.'

This was quite a new idea to Alice, and she thought it over a little before she made her next remark. 'Then the eleventh day must have been a holiday?'

'Of course it was,' said the Mock Turtle.

'And how did you manage on the twelfth?' Alice went on eagerly.

'That's enough about lessons,' the Gryphon interrupted in a very decided tone.

Why did the Gryphon not like talking about the twelfth day? Perhaps he didn't know negative numbers or numbers less than zero.

Ancient mathematicians didn't know about them either. Negative numbers first appeared in the works of the Indian mathematician Brahmagupta in 628. The French mathematician Blaise Pascal, famous for his work on probability (see p. 75), was convinced that such numbers could not exist. Many other contemporary mathematicians also considered them ridiculous. Nevertheless, by the eighteenth century negative numbers became an integral part of algebra.

Charles Lutwidge Dodgson (1832-98), who taught mathematics at Christ Church College, Oxford, wrote the Alice books under the pseudonym Lewis Carroll. The first Alice book began as a story told to Alice, Lorina and Edith young daughters of Henry George Lidell, the dean of Christ Church College, during an afternoon of rowing on the River Thames.

In *Alice's Adventures in Wonderland*, when Alice went down the rabbit-hole, she began to recite various things to reassure herself that she was still Alice:

I'll try if I know all the things I used to know. Let me see: four times five is twelve, and four times six is thirteen, and four times seven is — oh dear! I shall never get to twenty at that rate!

Why will Alice never get to twenty? Here Lewis Carroll is playing with number bases. Each product in Alice's multiplication table is in a different base. We count in base-10 (decimal system), computers in base-2 (binary system). Computer programmers also use base-16 hexadecimal system which uses digits 0 to 9 and letters A to F. Let's see Alice's multiplication table in different bases:

$4 \times 5 = 12$ (base-18)
$4 \times 6 = 13$ (base-21)
$4 \times 7 = 14$ (base-24)
$4 \times 8 = 15$ (base-27)
$4 \times 9 = 16$ (base-30)
$4 \times 10 = 17$ (base-33)
$4 \times 11 = 18$ (base-36)
$4 \times 12 = 19^*$ (base-39)
$4 \times 13 = 1\#$ (base-42)
$4 \times 14 = 1@$ (base-45)

* (in 19, 9 stands for 9 units; similarly # stands for 10 units and @ for 11 units; 1# above equals about 32 in base-10)

Oh dear! Alice's fancy multiplication table will never make it to twenty.

See also CYCLIC NUMBERS, p. 133.

# Painting by numbers

Four is the minimum number of colours required to colour any map in such a way that no two adjacent regions are to the same colour.

In 1852 a young law graduate of University College, London, named Francis Guthrie (1831-99) was colouring a map of the counties of England when the four-colour problem flashed across his mind.

He mentioned the problem to his brother Frederick who was then a student at the same college. Frederick could not solve the problem and asked his professor of mathematics, Augustus De Morgan (1806-71), for help. De Morgan, famous for De Morgan's theorem in logic, was also unable to find a solution. The problem first appeared in print in the *Proceedings of the London Mathematical Society* in 1878. A map, in this problem, is an arrangement of regions either on a planar or a spherical surface.

The problem occupied mathematicians for nearly a century. Everyone thought that they could easily solve the problem, which is comprehensible even to a school child, but failed miserably. In 1977 a University of Illinois supercomputer took 1,200 hours to solve the problem, which is now generally known as the four-colour theorem.

## Nine-rooms paradox

# Ten weary, footsore travellers

How did this clever innkeeper manage to accommodate ten
guests in nine single rooms with a room for each guest?

Ten weary, footsore travellers,
　All in a woeful plight,
Sought shelter at a wayside inn
　One dark and stormy night.

'Nine rooms, no more,' the landlord said
　'Have I to offer you.
To each of eight a single bed,
　But the ninth must serve for two.'

A din arose. The troubled host
　Could only scratch his head,
For of those tired men not two
　Would occupy one bed.

The puzzled host was soon at ease —
　He was a clever man —
And so to please his guests devised
　This most ingenious plan.

In room marked A two men were placed
The third was lodged in B,
　The fourth to C was then assigned,
The fifth retired to D.

　In E the sixth he tucked away,
In F the seventh man.
　The eighth and ninth in G and H,
And then to A he ran.

Wherein the host, as I have said,
　Had laid two travellers by;
Then taking one — the tenth and last —
　He logged him safe in I.

Nine single rooms — a room for each —
　Were made to serve for ten;
And this it is that puzzles me
　And many wiser men.

This classic puzzle — first
published in *Current Literature*
April 1889 — may seem
intriguing, but the answer (see p.
167) is amazingly simple.

In mathematics, a paradox is
a statement or proposition that
sounds reasonable but leads to
a self-contradictory conclusion.
A mathematical fallacy, on the
other hand, is a statement or
proposition that leads to a false
or absurd result because of
improper reasoning. Although,
known as nine-room paradox, it's
not really a paradox; it's a fallacy.

## The unexpected examination paradox

# No surprise exams!

A teacher tells the class that on one weekday of the following week she will give a surprise exam. Why can't she give a surprise exam?

This paradox, also known as the prediction paradox or the unexpected hanging paradox, has its origin in an episode during the Second World War.

The Swedish Broadcasting Service announced that a civil defence exercise would take place one day the following week. To ensure that all civil defence units were properly prepared, no one would know in advance what day this exercise would take place. Lennart Ekbom, a professor of mathematics at Ostermalms College in Stockholm, immediately realised that the announcement involved a logical paradox and discussed it with his students.

The paradox first appeared in print in 1948 in an article by the British philosopher D. J. O'Connor in the journal *Mind* (vol. LVII, pp. 358-9). Over the years the paradox has generated zillions of articles in respected journals without producing anything resembling a consensus as to the right solution.

Let's find out why. The surprise exam cannot be held on Friday, because on Thursday evening everyone will expect it to be held the following day as they hadn't had the exam during the week. An exam on Friday is not a surprise exam. Because students know that the exam cannot be held on Friday, it would have to be held on Thursday. But it cannot be held on Thursday, because by Wednesday evening students will know that the exam will be held either on Thursday or Friday. Again, there's no surprise. If we continue with this reasoning Wednesday, Tuesday and Monday are also out. So the teacher cannot give the surprise exam.

Of course, she can give a surprise exam.

## A geometric fallacy

# What's the trick?

An amazing geometric occurs when we form a square using the sum of two consecutive Fibonacci numbers as the lengths of the sides.

The square below has been formed by using the sum of two consecutive Fibonacci numbers (see p. 45) 3 and 5; that is, 8. Its area is 8 × 8 = 64 units. If you cut it up into four parts as shown, you can rearrange them into a rectangle with an area of 13 × 5 = 65 units. You have turned 64 units into 65 units. What's the trick?

It's hard to notice, but the diagonal of the rectangle is not a straight line. It has a bulge in the middle; it is, in fact, a parallelogram with an area of 1 unit. You can try this trick with the sum of any two consecutive Fibonacci numbers; for example, 5 and 8 to form a 13 × 13 square. A discrepancy of 1 unit alternates between the square and the rectangle depending on which consecutive numbers are used.

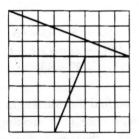

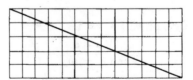

An algebraic fallacy

# How to prove that you're the Pope

Using mathematics to get an absurd result.

This story about the British mathematician and philosopher Bertrand Russell (see p. 116) is probably apocryphal, but it's worth telling. Russell once claimed that, given $1 + 1 = 1$, he could prove any other statement.

One day someone said to him, 'OK, prove that you are the Pope.' Russell thought for a moment and then said, 'I'm one. The Pope is one. Therefore the Pope and I are one.'

Let's prove $1 + 1 = 1$.

$$\text{If } a = b$$
$$\text{Then } a^2 = ab$$
$$a^2 + a^2 = a^2 + ab$$
$$2a^2 = a^2 + ab$$

Subtract $2ab$ from each side
$$2a^2 - 2ab = a^2 + ab - 2ab$$
$$= a^2 - ab$$
$$2(a^2 - ab) = 1(a^2 - ab)$$
Divide each side by $(a^2 - ab)$

$$2 = 1$$
$$\text{Or } 1 + 1 = 1$$

Look at this sum:
$$2 - 2 = 1 - 1$$
$$2(1 - 1) = 1 - 1$$
Divide each side by $(1 - 1)$
$$2 = 1$$

… and so on, proving any number equals any other number:

$$99 - 99 = 43 - 43$$
$$99(1 - 1) = 43(1 - 1)$$
$$99 = 43$$

Can you find the mistake? In the first sum, since $a = b$, dividing by $(a^2 - ab)$ is the same as dividing by zero. In the other sums, again, dividing by $(1 - 1)$ is dividing by zero. Dividing a number by zero is not allowed. It gives mathematicians a headache!

See also INFINITY, p. 13; ZERO, p. 15.

# The triangle that introduced fractals

The Sierpinski triangle, also known as the Sierpinski gasket, is a simple and interesting fractal formed from an equilateral triangle.

W aclaw Sierpinski (1882-1969) has been described as the greatest and most productive of Polish mathematicians. He wrote more than 700 papers and 50 books. Benoit Mandelbrot defined fractals in 1975 (see p. 127) long after Sierpinski had introduced his triangle in 1916. However, the underlying principle of the triangle had been known to Italian art since the thirteenth century.

To construct a Sierpinski triangle, first draw and fill an equilateral triangle (see diagram). Determine the mid-points of each side of the triangle. Use these mid-points to draw a new smaller triangle that divides the original equilateral triangle into four smaller equilateral triangles. Remove the middle triangle. Repeat the process with three remaining filled equilateral triangles. Theoretically the process can be repeated indefinitely.

# Inventors of brain twisters

Sam Loyd and Henry Dudeney are the two greatest
mathematical puzzle inventors of all time.

For or nearly half a century, until his death at 70 in 1911, Samuel Loyd (1841-1911) was America's undisputed puzzle king.

He became interested in mathematical and chess puzzles when he was fourteen years old and won many prizes for his puzzles while still at school. After leaving school he began studying engineering but never completed his studies as he found he could make a good living from creating puzzles. He produced more than 10,000 puzzles in his lifetime, of which 5,000 were included in his mammoth book, *Cyclopedia of Puzzles* (1914), compiled by his son, also named Sam, after his death.

In 1858, when he was a teenager, Loyd created a puzzle that became an instant commercial success and earned him $10,000 (an enormous sum in those days) within weeks. The puzzle, which he drew himself, was popularly known as trick donkeys. The problem is to cut the picture into three rectangles along the dotted lines, and rearrange the rectangles without folding them, to show two jockeys riding two galloping donkeys.

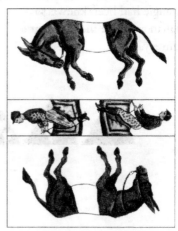

Sam Loyd's galloping donkeys puzzle.
Picture from Sam Loyd's
*Cyclopedia of Puzzles* (1914)

Loyd's most interesting puzzle was created in 1878. Known as the fifteen-puzzle, it consists of fifteen movable blocks which are arranged in a square box in rectangular order, but with the 14 and 15 reversed as shown in the picture. The objective is to move the blocks about, one at a time, to bring them back to the original position in every respect except that the error in the order of 14 and 15 is corrected.

The craze to solve the puzzle swept America and Europe where employers banned the puzzle during office hours. 'People became infatuated with the puzzle and ludicrous tales are told of shopkeepers who neglected to open their stores,' Loyd's son writes in *Cyclopedia*. 'The mysterious feature of the puzzle is that none seem able to remember the sequence of moves whereby they feel sure they have succeeded in solving the puzzle.'

The puzzle has no solution. It's still available and still infuriates people who try to solve it.

Henry Ernest Dudeney (1857-1930) was England's most eminent inventor of puzzles. When he was thirteen years old he joined the civil service as a clerk but continued to study mathematics. For nearly thirty years he ran a puzzle page, 'Perplexities', which he illustrated, in the *Strand* magazine. He published several books, including *Canterbury Puzzles* (1907), *Amusements in Mathematics* (1917) and *Modern Puzzles* (1926). He wrote in one of his books: 'The fact is that our lives are largely spent in solving puzzles; for what is a puzzle but a perplexing question?'

Dudeney's most fascinating mathematical teaser, the spider and the fly, first appeared in an English newspaper in 1903. In a rectangular room of 30 × 12 ×

| 1 | 2 | 3 | 4 |
| 5 | 6 | 7 | 8 |
| 9 | 10 | 11 | 12 |
| 13 | 15 | 14 | |

Sam Loyd's fifteen-puzzle

12 feet a spider is at the middle of an end wall, one foot from the ceiling. The fly is at the middle of the opposite end wall, one foot above the floor. The fly is too scared to move. What is the shortest distance the spider must crawl to capture the fly?

Answers to 'trick donkeys' and 'the spider and the fly' puzzles can be found on page 167.

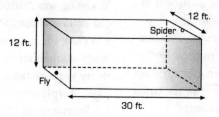

Dudeney's 'the spider and the fly' puzzle.

# When the world will vanish with a thunderclap

Tower of Hanoi is a puzzle based on a legend.

The puzzle was invented in 1883 by Édouard Lucas (1842-91), a professor of mathematics at the Lycée Saint Louis in Paris.

The puzzle consists of three pegs fixed to a disk. On one of these pegs rest eight discs of different sizes, stacked from largest to smallest. The problem is to shift the discs from this peg to either of the vacant pegs. Only one disc can be moved at one time and a disc cannot be placed on the top of a smaller one. For a tower of $n$ discs, the minimum number of moves required to shift all discs from one peg to another is $2^n - 1$. For a tower of eight discs it equals to 255 moves.

The puzzle was based on a Hindu legend which has it that in the city of Varanasi (Benares) on the river Ganges, there is a temple which marks the centre of world. Beneath the dome of the temple is to be found a brass plate on which are fixed three diamond needles. Brahma, the Hindu god of creation, placed sixty-four gold discs on one of the needles at the time of Creation. The discs are of different sizes and are stacked from largest to smallest. Day and night temple priests move one disc at a time to another needle so that there is no smaller disc below it. When the sixty-four discs have been moved to another needle, the whole universe will vanish with a thunderclap. The number of moves required in this case are $2^{64} - 1$ or 18,446,744,073,709,551,615. If the priests moves one disc every second, it would take more than 580 billion years to move all the discs. Don't panic! The universe is only 13.7 billion years old.

# Without being torn or cut

This 100-year-old maddeningly difficult puzzle has finally been solved.

The French mathematician Henri Poincaré (1854-1912) is generally regarded as the founder of topology, a branch of mathematics that is often described as 'rubber-sheet geometry'.

Topology deals with the properties of geometric shapes, such as the Möbius strip (see p. 110) and the Klein bottle (see p. 112), which can undergo arbitrary amounts of stretching and twisting without any change.

Consider a doughnut and a tea cup with a handle. Each has a single hole. By stretching and twisting — cutting and its opposite, sewing, are not allowed in topology — one can be manipulated to resemble the other. Poincaré called such an abstract topological space 'manifold'.

Now consider a soccer ball. It's a three-dimensional object, but each point on its surface looks like a two-dimensional space. To topologists, the soccer ball (or any sphere for that matter) is a 'two-dimensional manifold that is compact and simply connected'. Simple connectedness is the property topologists apply to all two-dimensional surfaces with no boundaries. Even when a soccer ball is stretched or crumpled, it has no hole. But a doughnut, on the other hand, has a hole. It's not a true sphere. A soccer ball cannot be turned into a doughnut or vice versa. If you tie a string around a soccer ball, you can easily pull the string closed. Topologists say that every path on the soccer ball could be shrunk to a point. But if you tie a string around a doughnut through the hole, you cannot pull the string closed without breaking either the string or the doughnut. For this reason, topologists say that the surface of a soccer ball is 'simply connected'.

Poincaré's conjecture is about abstract three-dimensional spheres. Is there a three-manifold that is different from the three-dimensional sphere and that has the property that every path can be shrunk to a point? Poincaré's conjecture says that there is no such manifold.

The question seems simple, but it has harassed mathematicians for nearly a century. The breakthrough came in 2002 when the Russian mathematician Grigori Perelman (b. 1966) posted the proof of the conjecture on the internet. It took mathematicians four years to reach the consensus that Perelman's proof is indeed correct. Perelman was awarded the prestigious Field Medal, the mathematical equivalent of the Nobel Prize, at the 2006 International Congress of Mathematician in Madrid. The reclusive mathematician declined the medal.

In 2000 the Clay Mathematics Institute at Cambridge, Massachusetts, named seven classical mathematics problems — including Poincaré's conjecture — that have resisted solution over the years. The Institute has announced a $1 million prize for each problem. The Institute has not yet offered the prize, popularly known as the millennium prize, to Perelman as it wants to ensure that there are no holes in his proof.

Poincaré once said: 'A scientist worthy of the name, above all a mathematician, experiences in his work the same impression as an artist; his pleasure is as great and of the same nature.' His conjecture will help scientists to describe the shape of the universe.

A true work of art!

See also KNOT THEORY, p. 128.

# Möbius strip

# A topological curiosity

A Möbius strip is a continuous loop which has only one
surface and one edge.

When you hold together
the two narrow ends of a
long, narrow rectangular strip
of paper, you get a familiar
cylindrical loop.

But if you give one end a
180-degree (that is, a half-way
round) twist so that the inside
surface meets the outside surface
and tape the two ends together,
you will now have a Möbius
strip (or band). This twisted
cylindrical loop has many unique
properties.

Start at any point of the
surface of your Möbius strip
and run your finger along the
surface, you will end up where
you started. You can try the same

with the edge. Cut the strip
down the middle all along its
length. Instead of splitting into
two loops, it turns into a single
large loop, twice as long, with
two half twists. It's no longer a
Möbius strip.

This amazing strip was
discovered in 1858 by the
German mathematician and
astronomer Augustus Möbius
(1790-1868). Now his strip lives
beyond mathematics — in art
(logos, postage stamps and in the
mathematical art of legendary
M. C. Escher), sculpture (a steel
sculpture at the Smithsonian
Museum in Washington, DC),
in a TV series (*Star Trek: Next
Generation*) and engineering
(conveyor and machinery belts
bases on Möbius strip wear and
tear on both sides equally).

It has also been a favourite of
limerick writers:

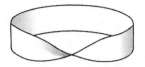

The Möbius strip

A burleycue dancer, a pip
Named Virgina, could peel a zip;
But she read science fiction
And died of consumption
Attempting a Möbius strip.

— American science fiction writer
*Cyril Kornbluth (1923-58)*

A mathematician confided
That a Möbius band is one-sided.
And you'll get quite a laugh
If you cut it in half,
For it stays in one piece when divided.

— *Unknown*

The topologist's mind came unguided
When his theories, some
   colleagues derided.
Out of Möbius strips
   Paper dolls he now snips,
Non-Euclidian, closed, and one-
   sided.

— American science fiction writer
*Hilbert Schenck Jr. (b. 1926)*

See also the POINCARÉ
CONJECTURE, p. 108;
KLEIN BOTTLE, p. 112.

# Another topological curiosity

*The Klein bottle has only one surface and no edges.*

The following limerick by an unknown, but mathematically minded, wag explains clearly the relationship between the Möbius strip (see p. 110) and the Klein bottle:

A mathematician named Klein
  Thought the Möbius band
    was divine.
Said he 'If you glue
  The edges of two,
You'll get a weird bottle like mine.'

This curious bottle has an outside but no inside; it passes through itself. It can't hold any liquid; if liquid were poured into it, it would come out of the same hole. The bottle was devised in 1882 by the German mathematician Felix Klein (1849-1925). Klein once said: 'The greatest mathematicians, as Archimedes, Newton, and Gauss, always united theory and applications in equal measure.' His weird bottle follows this trait of great mathematicians.

The Klein bottle

See also THE POINCARÉ CONJECTURE, p. 108.

## The Riemann hypothesis

# Key to cryptic codes

The famous Riemann hypothesis has tormented the world's greatest mathematicians for nearly 150 years. It still remains unsolved.

In 1859 Bernhard Riemann (1826-66), a shy thirty-three-year-old German mathematician, published an eight-page-article entitled, in translation, 'On the number of prime numbers under a given magnitude' in the monthly notices of the Berlin Academy for November.

In this article he gave a possible answer to a highly complex problem about the random distribution of prime numbers. Today we know of the first 1.5 billion prime numbers. They do not follow any regular pattern; the numbers are distributed randomly. The Riemann hypothesis is to give a formula which will state where every single prime number to infinity will occur.

Prime numbers not only amuse pure mathematicians, but these days they also have a very important practical application. They are the key to cryptic codes, which keep internet commerce secure. The cracking of the Riemann hypothesis could ruin internet banking and other commercial transactions. If cryptic codes could be broken, no internet transaction would be safe.

In 2000 the Clay Mathematics Institute at Cambridge, Massachusetts, named seven classical mathematics problems that have resisted solution over the years. The Institute has announced a $1 million prize for each problem. This prize is now popularly known as the millennium prize. The Riemann Hypothesis is one of the seven 'holy grails' of mathematics.

See also PRIME NUMBERS, p. 37; THE POINCARÉ CONJECTURE, p. 108.

Curved space

# 'The grin of the Cheshire cat'

The concept of curved space takes us beyond Euclidean geometry's flat space.

Bernhard Riemann (see p. 113) was one of the first mathematicians to study curved space. His work created a new geometry now known as Riemann geometry or elliptical geometry.

Unlike Euclid's geometry (see p. 20), Riemann geometry is directly connected to our daily lives as we live on a curved surface — the planet Earth which inhabits a curved universe. In Riemann geometry there are no true parallel lines, all straight lines are equal in length, and the sum of angles of a triangle is always greater than 180 degrees. The last idea allows all longitudinal lines to cross at both the North and South poles.

Albert Einstein (1879-1955) was highly impressed by Riemann's idea of curved space and applied it in his general theory of relativity. The theory, published in 1915, stated that bodies do not attract each other by exerting a pull, but that the presence of matter in space causes space to curve in such a manner that a gravitational field is set up.

Gravity is a property of space itself and even light is bent by gravity. Matter and energy determine how space and space-time (three dimensions of space and the fourth dimension of time) are curved. Space and curvature determine how matter moves. At the end stage of the curvature of space-time, space is so curved that once matter and energy enter that space, they can never get out. This is the 'black hole', a point of infinite density where mass has no volume and both time and space stops. Nothing — not even light — can escape a black hole.

At first it was thought that black holes were an abstract mathematical idea, but it is now well known that black holes actually exist, just as Einstein's theory predicts.

Riemann geometry does not mean that Euclidean geometry is wrong. Euclidean geometry works accurately as long as the curvature is small. The noted British astrophysicist Arthur Eddington (1882-1944) explains how geometers and physicists see the curved space:

To the pure geometer the radius of curvature is an incidental characteristic — like the grin of the Cheshire cat. To the physicist it is an indistinguishable characteristic. It would be going too far to say that to the physicist the cat is merely incidental to the grin. Physics is concerned with the interrelatedness such as the interrelatedness of cats and grins. In this case the 'cat without a grin' and the 'grin without a cat' are equally set aside as purely mathematical phantasies.

— *The Expanding Universe (1933)*

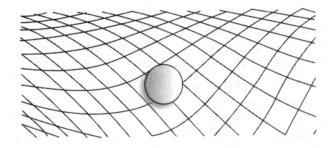

## Russell's paradox

# Who shaves the barber?

Russell's paradox is the most famous of logical paradoxes.

The paradox comes from set theory (see p. 83). Sets either are or are not members themselves.

Consider S, a set that contains members which are (a) sets; and (b) not members of themselves. Is S a member of S? If S is a member of S, then it fails to meet the requirement to not be a member of itself. But if S is not a member of S, then it meets the requirement to be a member of S. This is the contradiction.

The paradox was proposed in 1902 by Bertrand Russell (1872-1970), a philosopher and mathematician and the future winner of the 1950 Nobel prize for literature. To explain the paradox to non-mathematicians, Russell proposed in 1918 the 'barber paradox'. A village barber has the following sign on his shop: 'I shave only and all men in the village who do not shave themselves'. Does the barber shave himself? If he does shave himself, he would belong to the set of men who shave themselves, meaning he shouldn't shave himself. If he doesn't shave himself and decides to wear a full beard, then he should do so according to the sign. This is the barber's predicament, at least, until he takes the sign down.

Russell wrote to Gottlob Frege (1848-1925), a German mathematician and logician, with the news of paradox in 1902. The second volume of Frege's text on the logical development of arithmetic was in press. Frege was 'thunderstruck' as the paradox showed inconsistencies in the axioms he was using to formalise his logic. He quickly added an appendix and wrote in preface: 'A scientist can hardly encounter anything more undesirable than to have the foundation collapse just as the work is finished.'

Srinivasa Ramanujan

# 'The Indian Clerk'

Ramanujan is considered by many to have possessed one
of the most beautiful mathematical minds of the past few
centuries.

In 1913, G. H. Hardy (1877 1947), a prominent English mathematician of the past century, received a nine-page letter filled with complex number theorems from Srinivasa Ramanujan (1887-1920), an obscure accounts clerk in Madras, India.

Hardy was so spellbound with the mathematical genius of the self-taught clerk that he immediately arranged for him to come to Cambridge University to work with him. The story of their collaboration and friendship is heart-warming and is beautifully told in *The Indian Clerk* (2007), a novel by David Leavitt, an English professor at the University of Florida.

The climate of England did not suit Ramanujan and he returned to India in 1919. He died a year later at the age of thirty-two. Though he published many papers in renowned journals, Ramanujan's legacy is his notebooks: 400 pages densely packed with 4,000 formulas and theorems of incredible power, but without any commentary. Nearly ninety years later mathematicians are still struggling to decipher his incandescent genius.

It is said that every integer was Ramanujan's personal friend. During an illness in England, Hardy visited Ramanujan in the hospital. 'The number of my cab was 1729. It seemed to me rather a dull number,' remarked Hardy. Ramanujan immediately responded: 'No, Hardy! It's a very interesting number. It's the smallest integer that can be expressed as the sum of two cubes in two different ways.' He meant $1729 = 1^3 + 12^3 = 9^3 + 10^3$.

Ramanujan once said: 'An equation for me has no meaning unless it expresses a thought of God.'

## The Turing machine

# An imaginary computer

### The Turing machine is a theoretical universal machine that could perform mathematical calculations.

In 1937, while working at Cambridge University, the brilliant British mathematician Alan Turing (1912-54), now famous for breaking the German navy's Enigma code during the Second World War, proposed a theoretical computer that obeyed instructions sets out in an algorithm (see p. 36).

The machine has two or more states and reacts to an input to produce an output. The method of applying an input to obtain an output is called a computation.

The theoretical machine, now known as the Turing machine, consists of a box with a tape of infinite length divided into cells each inscribed with a symbol from a finite alphabet (that has a blank symbol). A read-write head is always located exactly over one of these cells. It can read or write to a cell in its current location, and also move cell by cell either way along the tape. The machine has an algorithm that specifies each move based on the current state and the symbol under the current cell. The following diagram, for example, shows two states of a Turing machine. When it is in state 0 scanning A, the machine will move right one square and return to state 0. When it is in state 0 scanning B, it will change B to A and go into state 1.

The Turing machine is the precursor to the computers we use today; and the pioneering mathematician is considered to be the founder of modern computer science.

The Turing machine

# Burglars' dilemma

Game theory uses mathematics and logic in situations that involve people with conflicting interests.

In other words, the theory is concerned with how rational individuals make decisions when they are placed in competitive situations.

The theory originated in 1937 when the American mathematician John von Neumann (1903-57) realised that parlour games such as poker were not guided by probability theory (see p. 75) alone, and that 'bluffing', a strategy to hide information from other players, was also crucial. He further developed the theory in 1944 with the American mathematician Oskar Morgenstern (1902-76). Their theory applied to cooperative games: how groups of individual committed to each other formulate rational decisions.

In 1949, John Nash (b. 1928), while studying for his PhD at Princeton University, extended the theory to real-world situations of non-cooperative games in which individuals are unable to enter into binding and enforceable agreements with each other. A few years later Nash was diagnosed with paranoid schizophrenia. His subsequent tragic life story is the subject of German economist Sylvia Nasar's book *A Beautiful Mind* (1998) and the Oscar-winning movie of the same name (2001) starring Russell Crowe. Nash, who was awarded the 1994 Nobel Prize for economics, has now recovered and still works at Princeton.

Game theory has now been applied to a diverse range of issues in economics, computer science, psychology, sociology, biology, anthropology, politics, warfare, the stock market and many other fields.

In game theory all games have three things in common: rules, strategies and playoffs. Games include zero-sum games (each player benefits at the expense of others), non-zero-sum games (the sum of gains and losses is more or less than what the game begins with), cooperative games (people can make bargains) and non-cooperative games (people are unable to make enforceable contracts). The equilibrium of a game is called Nash equilibrium, a solution that maximises everyone's benefit. Nash equilibrium is considered game theory's most important aspect.

The prisoner's dilemma, a game described below, is a popular example of a non-zero sum non-cooperative game.

Two burglars, who were caught red-handed with stolen goods, are held in two separate cells at a remand centre. The interviewing officer gives each of them the following three options:

- If you plead guilty, but your partner doesn't, you will receive a $500 reward, but your partner will be fined $1,000.
- If you both plead guilty, you will both be fined $500.
- If neither of you plead guilty, both will go free, but there will be no reward.

If the burglars are familiar with the game theory, they will analyse as follows:

|  | My partner pleads guilty | My partner doesn't plead guilty |
|---|---|---|
| I plead guilty | -500, -500 | 500 |
| I plead not guilty | -1000, 500 | 0 |

The shaded cell is called the saddle point; it is simultaneously a minimum in its row and a maximum in its column. It's the equilibrium decision point and represents a decision by two players that neither can improve upon it by unilaterally departing from it. According to this decision point, each burglar will plead guilty and will be fined $500.

We can combine the two play-off tables making it a cooperative game:

|  | My partner pleads guilty | My partner doesn't plead guilty |
|---|---|---|
| I plead guilty | -500, -500 | 500, -1000 |
| I plead not guilty | -1000, 500 | 0, 0 |

It's clear that the burglars would have been better if they could have cooperated. They both would have pleaded not guilty.

## Paul Erdös

# 'My brain is open'

One of the greatest — and most eccentric —
mathematicians of the twentieth century who breathed
mathematics for most of his life.

Paul Erdös (1913-96) was a most prolific mathematician. A really great mathematician may publish 50 papers in a lifetime; Erdös published more than 1,500 papers and collaborated with 460 mathematicians. He never held a 'proper job', never owned a house, had almost no personal possessions, wrote no best-selling book; yet he was the member of many prestigious institutions such as the Royal Society and received numerous honours and prizes, including the prestigious Wolf prize. He always donated the prize money to help students or as prizes for solving mathematical problems he had posted.

For the most of his adult life he travelled from city to city, wearing sandals and an old suit and carrying two well-worn suitcases, each half-full. He stayed with mathematician colleagues wherever he went. He would arrive at their houses unannounced, and knock on the door with the greeting: 'My brain is open'. In return for their hospitality, he showered them with problems and rare mathematical insights. His colleagues revered him, always eager to work with the witty, friendly and inspiring genius.

Erdös solved many complex problems in number theory, geometry, graph theory, combinatorics, set theory, function theory and many other areas. He created a new area of inquiry now referred to as discrete mathematics, which is the foundation of computer science. He was not an abstract mathematician; instead of devising theories, he loved solving and posing problems. The German-American mathematician Ernst Straus (1922-83), who worked both with Einstein and Erdös, called Erdös 'the prince of problem solvers and the absolute monarch of problem posers'.

## Gödel's incompleteness theorems
# True and false at the same time

**In a formal theory there always exists a statement that cannot be proved within the theory even though its truth is apparent.**

This is one of the many simple versions of the two incompleteness theorems presented and proved by the Austrian mathematician Kurt Gödel (1906-78). The theorems, which shocked the mathematical world when they were unveiled in 1931, are considered the most important mathematical discovery of the previous 100 years.

The theorems imply that it is possible to construct an axiom, a self-evident truth that requires no proof, which is neither provable nor disprovable in any system based on a complete set of axioms. Thus, a mathematical theorem can be constructed which can be both true and false at the same time.

Some people have extended Gödel's theorems to argue that a computer can never be as smart as a human being. A computer can only operate by a given set of rules or axioms. It can never decide whether a statement is true if the statement can't be proved by its fixed set of rules. Human beings, on the other hand, can recognise that the statement is true even if it can't be proved logically. Human beings can discover unexpected truths.

Mathematicians are known for their eccentricities, but Gödel's eccentricities are legendary. In his later years he withdrew from all human contact and received communications only through a door in his office. There are numerous stories about him. On one occasion, he was required to fill a bureaucratically designed form. As he read the form he became increasingly frustrated. Instead of giving 'yes' and 'no' answers, he wrote a long essay for each question, explaining that if the question meant X the answer was A, but if the question meant Y, the answer was B, and so on.

# A prediction tool

A mathematical model is a mathematical representation of a
particular real-world phenomenon such as global warming.

A mathematical model
consists of equations and
step-by-step rules that reflect
what happens in a real event.

A model is never perfect and
mathematicians and scientists
continually update their models
on the basis of new observations.

This updating process
continues in a cycle as shown
in the diagram. In stage 1, the
modeller collects data about the
phenomenon and then presents
it in precise mathematical
language. Stages 2 and 3 are used
to test the model by making
mathematical predictions
about the phenomenon. The
predictions may be either about

previously observed situations
or some unknown situations.
In stage 4, these predictions
are now translated from the
mathematical language of the
model to the language of the
real world. These predictions
are then checked against the real
data. The model is now modified
and the cycle starts again. Note
that predictions are based on
deduction which is a logical
process in which a theory is used
to generate specific information.
Translation is by induction which
is a logical process used to build a
general statement from a series of
related observations. Hypothesis
is a stage beyond induction.

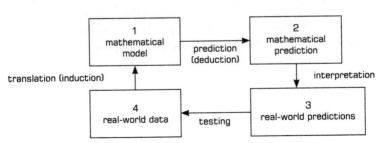

# 'A lot of interesting angles'

Exponential curves are used to model growth, such as population growth.

T he American actress Mae West (1893-1980) once quipped: 'A figure with curves always offers a lot of interesting angles.'

An exponential curve offers many more angles as it provides a window into growth (such as population growth, growth of bacteria) and decay (such as radioactive decay) of things.

An exponential is a function that varies with power (exponent) of another quantity. In $y = a^x$ (where $a$ is any number greater than zero), $y$ varies exponentially with $x$, the exponent. When $x$ increases, $y$ grows rapidly (see diagram). This is called exponential growth.

If $a$ is a fraction, say $a = \frac{1}{2}$, in the graph of $y = (\frac{1}{2})x$ (which is

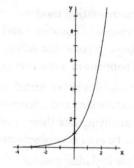

the same as $y = 2 - x$), $y$ decreases rapidly when $x$ increases. This type of curve is used to model radioactive decay, for instance.

If you still do not understand exponential curves, Felix Klein (of the Klein bottle fame, see p. 112) explains the reason why: 'Everyone knows what a curve is, until he has studied enough mathematics to become confused through the countless number of possible exceptions.'

# A theory for the Information Age

Information theory is the study of information transmission and reception using mathematical models. The term is sometimes used synonymously with communication theory.

In 1948 Claude Shannon (1916-2001), a mathematician at Bell Telephones in the United States, published a paper 'A Mathematical Theory of Communication' in which he introduced the revolutionary idea, now so familiar to us, that pictures, words and sounds could be transmitted by a stream of 0s and 1s. He called each 0 or 1 a bit (short for 'binary digit'). His paper laid the foundation of a new theory of communications — now known as information theory.

This theory is at the heart of compression and reliable transmission of data on the internet, in landline and wireless telephone systems and storage devices from computer hard disks to DVDs.

To us 'information' is 'useful knowledge' but in information theory information is carried by messages. Every message has three parts: a sender, a channel and a receiver. The message is sent in a string of zeros and ones. Shannon said that transmission errors could be corrected by adding extra bits to a message, and the message would arrive at the receiver's end without any loss of information.

Applications of information theory are now not limited to transmission of data. In physics it is applied to the entropy of a system. Entropy is a measure of disorder or randomness of a system. In genetics it is applied to information carried by DNA from generation to generation. Geneticists view each three-letter code word of DNA as a message.

All this and more has sprung up from a visionary mathematician who saw 0s and 1s as the fundamental elements of information.

# Fuzzy logic
# Shades of grey

Fuzzy logic is a mathematical way of dealing with imprecise
data and problems that have more than one solution.

Digital computers are built on Boolean logic (see p. 90) which applies to binary values, 1 or 0, yes or no, true or false. This logic works well for computers but fails miserably in the real world.

Fuzzy logic provides us a way of dealing with the question: 'To what degree is something true or false?' In fuzzy logic values are indicated in the range from 0 to 1 where 0 represents absolutely false and 1 absolutely true. Thus, fuzzy logic can deal with shades of grey between true and false.

Fuzzy logic began in 1965 when Russian-born Lotfi Zadeh (b. 1921), a professor of computer science at the University of California at Berkley, published a paper on 'Fuzzy Sets', which was an extension of set theory (see p. 83).

In this paper Zadeh named fuzzy sets as those sets whose boundaries are not clear, such as a 'set of beautiful people'. An object is either in a set or not. There is no middle ground: either you belong to the 'set of beautiful people' or you don't. Set theory refuses the membership, but fuzzy logic allows everyone some degree of membership because it does not measure membership as 0 or 1, but as between 0 and 1.

Zadeh was not the first to look for the shades of grey. The great Greek philosopher Plato (c. 429-c. 347 BC) also believed in a third region beyond 'true' and 'false' where opposites 'tumbled about'. But Zadeh was the first to give this concept a mathematical precise definition.

# The geometry of roughness

Fractals are self-similar shapes that appear essentially the same at different magnifications.

Euclid's geometry describes ideal shapes — the square, the triangle, the circle, the cube, the sphere, and so on. Most patterns in the real world are not formed of such simple geometric figures, but of shapes that have rough edges. Euclidean geometry cannot describe the shape of a coastline, a cloud, a mountain range, a snowflake or tree bark.

In 1975 Polish-American mathematician Benoit Mandelbrot (b. 1924) coined the word 'fractal' (from the Latin *fractus*, 'broken') to describe natural shapes that are self-similar and appear the same as you zoom in and zoom out. Ferns, cauliflowers, snowflakes, rivers, mountains, clouds — they all are fractals. Fractal geometry is the geometry of these irregular shapes in which fractals are described by mathematical equations that can be used to generate computer images. Fractal geometry can be used to model and describe, though not to predict, many complex phenomena such global climate change, earthquakes and hurricanes, water and air turbulence, galaxy clusters and ups and downs of stock markets.

'Being a language, mathematics may be used not only to inform but also, among other things, to seduce,' says Mandelbrot. Fractal geometry is a new language. Once you speak it you can describe the shape of a cloud as precisely as an architect a house.

See also SIERPINSKI TRIANGLE, p. 103.

# Unknotting the knot

Knot theory is a recent field of topology which studies the actual structure of knots.

'A knot,' said Alice. 'Oh, do let me help to undo it.'

— Lewis Carroll, *Alice's Adventures in Wonderland* (1865)

What's so special about knots that mathematicians have knotted a theory around them?

Knots are everywhere. They allow DNA molecules to replicate easily. DNA consists of a double helix of two strands coiled around each other. When the strands are uncoiled, they provide two copies of the original. This unique structure explains how DNA stores genetic information and how it passes this information on to the next generation by making an identical copy of itself. Knot theory is helping scientists to understand what type of knotting allows DNA to replicate so easily. Knots are used in chemistry to distinguish

between chemical elements by visualising their atoms as distinct knotted vortices. In physics, the so-called string theories explain the nature of the universe in terms of one-dimensional objects called strings which are knotted. The configurations of these knots are used to describe the different interactions between fundamental particles.

To us a knot is just a knotted loop of string, but to mathematicians it's a closed curve in space that does not intersect itself anywhere. It cannot exist in more than three dimensions. A mathematical knot has no thickness and therefore its cross-section is a single point. Mathematicians also imagine them as if they were made of easily deformed rubber. Deforming a knot doesn't change it, for mathematicians, at least.

The simplest possible knot is just the unknotted circle, which is called the unknot or the trivial knot. Next comes the trefil knot. It has three crossings and comes in left- and right-handed versions which are mirror images of one another.

There is only one knot with four crossings. Two types of knots have been identified with five crossings, three types with six crossings, seven types with seven crossings, and so on up to sixteen crossings with 1,388,705 types of knots. Boffins are still working on higher crossings. In the meantime, T. S. Eliot (*The Family Reunion*, 1939) has summed up the knot theory nicely:

Round and round the circle
   Completing the charm
So the knot be unknotted
   The cross uncrossed
The crooked be made straight
   And the curse be ended.

See also THE POINCARÉ CONJECTURE, p. 108.

The unknot (left) and the trefil knot.

# Six-sided magic

After more than three decades Rubik's cube still challenges
mathematicians — and supercomputers.

Rubik's cube is made up from 27 little cubes in a 3 × 3 × 3 arrangement. Each little cube is internally hinged in such a way that each of its six sides will rotate about its centre. Each of these sides is painted in a different colour. In an original Rubik's cube, each of the six sides, consisting of nine little cubes, is in a single colour. After a few random rotations colours are mixed up. The goal of the puzzle is to get the disordered cube to its original state.

The Hungarian architect Ernö Rubik invented the cube in 1974 and it was first marketed in 1977. Since then more than 300 million cubes have been sold worldwide. Solving the puzzle seems simple, but there are more than 43 million trillion different arrangements of the small cubes. The minimum number of moves required to solve any scrambled

Rubik's cube is sometimes called 'God's number' (obviously God would only need the smallest number to solve a cube). Theory suggests that this number is in the low 20s. In the 1990s the upper limit of 29 was produced, followed by an upper limit of 27 in 2006.

In 2007 a supercomputer at Northeastern University in Boston spent 63 hours to prove that a Rubik's cube can be returned to its original state in 26 moves. Mathematicians believe that we have not yet reached God's number. Supercomputer ought to work harder.

# Seven subtle shapes

A tangram is a puzzle composed of seven pieces.

These seven pieces — one square, five triangles and one rhombus — are cut from a square as shown in the diagram:

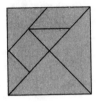

The seven pieces can be used to made an enormous number of shapes, as seen below.

Known as *qiqiaotu* (seven subtle shapes), tangrams have been popular in China for thousands of years. A similar puzzle was known to ancient Greeks, including Archimedes. The name tangram was coined in the mid-nineteenth century by an American toy manufacturer.

# Send more money

Cryptoarithmetic puzzles are some of the most challenging
verbal puzzles.

**C** ryptoarithmetic puzzles are algebraic equations where individual letters can be replaced by digits 0 to 9.

In these puzzles each letter represents a unique digit. As in ordinary arithmetic, no leading zeros are allowed; that is, the first digit of a multi-digit number cannot be zero. The puzzles usually have only one solution.

The most famous cryptoarithmetic puzzle was conceived in 1924 by Ernest Dudeney (see. p. 106):

```
  SEND
+ MORE
 MONEY
```

The only solution of this puzzle is S = 9, E = 5, N = 6, D = 7, M = 1, O = 0, R = 8, Y = 2. Or

```
  9567
+ 1085
 10652
```

You may try these puzzles (answers on p. 167):

```
  ONE
+ ONE
  TWO
```

```
 FORTY
+ TEN
+ TEN
 SIXTY
```

# Repeating sequence of digits

Cyclic numbers are one of the most remarkable of whole numbers.

A cyclic number repeats itself endlessly, it is an integer which, when multiplied by 1, 2, 3... *n* produces the same digits in a cyclic order. The best known and the smallest cyclic number is 142857:

$$142857 \times 1 = 142857$$
$$142857 \times 2 = 285714$$
$$142857 \times 3 = 428571$$
$$142857 \times 4 = 571428$$
$$142857 \times 5 = 714285$$
$$142857 \times 6 = 857142$$

But when it is multiplied by 7, the answer is a six-digit number, but still amazing:

$$142857 \times 7 = 999999$$

Cyclic numbers occur when a prime number, say *p*, and its reciprocal 1/*p* in decimal form is recurring with (*p* − 1) digits.

The first prime number with this property is 7, and 1/7 gives

$$0.142857142857...$$

(the dots imply that this repeating pattern goes on forever)

This is also written as 0.142857 (the dot over 7 meaning that the pattern repeats forever, and is called 'repeater'). One-third in decimals is 0.3 or 0.3333...

Prime numbers 17, 19, 23, 29, 47, 59, 61, and 97 also have this property and the next eight cyclic numbers can be obtained by finding their reciprocals. All cyclic numbers generated by these prime numbers begin with one or more zeros. For example, 1/17 gives 0.0588235294117647...

or the sixteen-digit cyclic number 0588235294117647

When multiplied by numbers 1 to 16 the number is repeated in a cyclic order, but when multiplied by 17 the answer is — not surprisingly — a seventeen-digit row of

99999999999999999

Another interesting property of cyclic numbers is that they all have an even number of digits and, when split in half give two numbers which always add up to a row of 9s:

$$
\begin{array}{r}
0\,5\,8\,8\,2\,3\,5\,2 \\
9\,4\,1\,1\,7\,6\,4\,7 \\
\hline
9\,9\,9\,9\,9\,9\,9\,9
\end{array}
$$

Ethel Cowell, to whom Lewis Carroll (see p. 94) taught logic when she was young, says in her book *Time and Time Again* (1941) how the Mad Hatter's Party in *Alice's Adventures in Wonderland* (1865) illustrates the idea of cyclic numbers:

'Then you keep moving round, I suppose?' said Alice.
'Exactly so,' said the Hatter: 'as the things get used up.'
'But what happens when you come to the beginning again?' Alice ventured to ask.

Well, Alice, you start again and again...

# How many squares are on a chessboard?

The answer is definitely not 64.

According to a popular story, a king of ancient India was so excited about the discovery of chess that he granted the inventor of the game one wish.

The wily inventor said that he wanted one grain of rice on the first square, two grains on the second square, four on the third, eight on the fourth and so on through the 64th square. The unwitting king agreed to the modest request. But 2-to-the-power-of-64 ($2^{64}$) is an extremely large number: 18,446,744,073,709,551,616. The number of rice grains would be more than enough to cover the whole surface of the earth. The king, the story goes, realising his mistake, ordered the inventor beheaded.

Now to our question. The chessboard has 64 one-unit squares which do not overlap. But if we start counting overlapping squares we will find that it also has 49 two-unit squares (each two-unit square consists of 4 one-unit squares), 36 three-unit squares (each of which consists of 9 one-unit squares) and so on. The sum of all the one-unit squares, the two-unit squares and the three-unit squares is $8^2 + 7^2 + 6^2$. If we continue with our calculations we will come up with the series which gives the answer:

$$8^2 + 7^2 + 6^2 + 5^2 + 4^2 + 3^2 + 2^2 + 1^2 = 204$$

Perhaps the inventor was hoping to be paid for 204 squares; that is, $2^{204}$ grains, a number much bigger than googol (see p. 139).

# How many sudokus?

Sudoku means 'single numbers' in Japanese.

A Sudoku is a 9 × 9 grid made of nine 3 × 3 boxes. The cells in each box are filled with numbers 1 to 9 so that no row, column or diagonal contains the same numbers twice, as shown below:

| 4 | 6 | 8 | 9 | 2 | 7 | 3 | 1 | 5 |
|---|---|---|---|---|---|---|---|---|
| 9 | 2 | 1 | 6 | 5 | 3 | 8 | 4 | 7 |
| 5 | 7 | 3 | 1 | 4 | 8 | 2 | 6 | 9 |
| 3 | 1 | 5 | 4 | 8 | 6 | 9 | 7 | 2 |
| 6 | 8 | 9 | 2 | 7 | 1 | 4 | 5 | 3 |
| 7 | 4 | 2 | 3 | 9 | 5 | 6 | 8 | 1 |
| 2 | 5 | 7 | 8 | 3 | 4 | 1 | 9 | 6 |
| 1 | 9 | 4 | 7 | 6 | 2 | 5 | 3 | 8 |
| 8 | 3 | 6 | 5 | 1 | 9 | 7 | 2 | 4 |

A Sudoku-like puzzle, called the Number Place, first appeared in the United States in 1979. The puzzle was subsequently introduced in Japan in 1984.

In 1997 Wayne Gould, a New Zealander and retired judge living in Hong Kong, was mesmerised when he saw a partially completed puzzle in a Japanese bookshop. He spent six years writing a computer program that automatically generates Sudoku grids. In 2004 the *London Times* introduced the puzzle in its pages. In 2005 *The New York Post* became the first American newspaper to publish the puzzle daily.

Keh-Ying Lin, a physics professor at the National Tsing Hua University in Taiwan, has determined that the total number of sudokus is 6,670,903,752,021,072,936,960. A comforting fact for Sudoku addicts!

See also MAGIC SQUARES, p. 68.

# As simple as tic-tac-toe

Not really, tic-tac-toe is a game of skill.

It's as simple as tit-tat-toe, three-in-a-row, and as easy as playing hooky. I should hope we can find a way that's a little more complicated than that, Huck Finn.

— Mark Twain in *The Adventures of Huckleberry Finn* (1884)

Tic-tac-toe, also known as noughts and crosses, and spelt in many different ways, is a pencil-and-paper game for two players.

It may have its origin in older games, but Charles Babbage was the first to describe its rules in about 1820. He called it tit-tat-to and designed a machine to play the game. Like his differential and analytical engines, it was never built (see p. 91).

As you know, in tic-tac-toe two players take turns to mark either O or X on one of the nine cells in a 3 × 3 grid. The player who first places three identical marks in a horizontal, vertical or diagonal row wins the game. Though there are 255,168 possible games, you cannot win the game against an expert opponent. An expert player will always draw, as tic-tac-toe is a zero-sum game (see p. 119).

Some winning tips if you are playing against a novice:

- If you are the first to start, begin with a corner cell.

- If your opponent starts with centre opening, counter the move by occupying a corner cell.

- If your opponent occupies any cell (a) next to you, choose the centre cell; (b) horizontally or vertically opposite cell, choose the cell that is diagonally opposite to you; (c) any other cell, choose the cell opposite your first cell.

# Mathematics to the ears

Music and mathematics have been inextricably linked since sixth century BC.

Pythagoras, now chiefly remembered for the theorem that bears his name (see p. 24), was the first to apply mathematics to music.

Legend has it that he linked music to mathematics when he was walking by a blacksmith's shop and heard the sounds of several hammers striking the anvil. Different notes were produced for hammers of different weights. He wondered whether different notes were related to the weights of the hammer.

He and his followers, known as Pythagoreans, made simple experiments on the sound produced by plucking a stretched string and found that the pitch of the note depended on the length of the vibrating string. They also found that the tones were harmonious when the lengths of the vibrating strings were in the ratio of simple whole numbers such as 2:3 or 3:4, and an entire musical scale could be produced by taking whole number ratios of a string's length. They were the first to show that musical harmony was a mathematical property.

The French mathematician Jean Baptise Joseph Fourier (1768-1830), known to students of higher mathematics for his Fourier series, discovered a method that can be applied to the analysis of a musical sound. He realised that any periodic oscillation, such as a sound wave, can be broken up into a set of simple sine curves defined by the function $y = \sin(x)$. These sine curves can be used to describe the pattern of any kind of wave.

Now the links between music and mathematics have become stronger than ever. Today's music is digital, at least the way it is recorded, compressed, stored, transmitted and listened to.

# Google googol

And you will find a very large number, indeed.

The word 'googol' has an interesting history. When the American mathematician Edward Kasner (1878-1955) asked his nine-year-old nephew Milton Sirotta what name he would give to a very large number, he replied 'googol'. Kasner used the word for the number $10^{100}$ (1 followed by 100 zeros). That was in 1938. Since then the word has caught public's fancy and is often bandied about when we talk about large numbers. The search engine Google is a play on the word googol.

Kasner later extended googol to even larger 'googolplex' which is equal to 1 followed by a googol number of zeros, or

$$10^{\text{googol}} \text{ or } 10^{10^{100}}$$

The largest number that you can write with just three digits is not 999 or $99^9$ or even $9^{99}$. It's

$$9^{9^9}$$

The figure expresses 9 raised to the 9th power of 9. As $9^9$ is 387420489, the number can be written as $9^{387420489}$. The answer contains 369 million digits. Eat your heart out, googol! It's a number crying out for a name. Rise to the challenge, if you're nine years old.

$$1 \text{ googol} = 10000000...$$

# The rocket science of loan payment

A simple way to reduce the total amount of interest on mortgage loans.

I n the 1970s 'rocket scientists' (physicists and engineers who began to work in the financial markets after the downscaling of NASA's space program) applied complex mathematical modelling to understand how finance markets work and how the economy behaves.

A mathematical model is a mathematical version of a real-life situation. It's realistic enough to provide a good picture of the real-life situation but is simpler to work with than the real-life situation.

Mathematical modelling is not only relevant to large financial institutions. Even individuals can apply it to make informed financial decisions. In mortgage loans payments the reducing balance method is used to calculate the payment of each monthly instalment. You pay interest on what you owe

each month instead of the total amount borrowed. The complex formula used to calculate monthly mortgage payments is a simple mathematical model that shows the relationship between monthly payments ($Q$) and the total number of months needed to pay the loan ($n$). The model reveals that a slight increase in $Q$ will result in a large decrease in $n$. For example, the monthly payments for a loan of $100,000 at 6% over 15 years are $844. If the loan payment is increased by $100 per month to $944, the loan would be fully paid in 12.5 years instead of 15 years. And your total interest amount will reduce from $51,920 to $41,600.

So, the lesson from 'rocket scientists' is that when paying off a mortgage loan try to pay a little bit extra each month instead of the minimum monthly amount.

# A matter of interest

This rule-of-thumb makes compound interest calculations simple.

Einstein was once asked to name the greatest discovery of the twentieth century. Most expected him to refer to nuclear energy or some other scientific discovery, but his answer was compound interest. The story is probably apocryphal but it highlights the importance of compound interest.

The rule of 72 says that in order to find the number of years required to double your money at a given compound interest rate, you can just divide 72 by the annual interest rate. For example, to find out how long would it take to double your money at 8% interest, divide 72 by 8 and you get 9 years. The rule also works backwards. You can use it to calculate the interest rate if you know your money would double in so-and-so many years by dividing 72 by the number of years. For example, to double $2,000 in 5 years, you need to invest it at an interest rate of 72/5 = 14.4%. But if you save $2,000 per year for the next five years only and earn 10% compound interest per year on your savings, you would have more than $57,000 after 20 years. The interest is a whopping $47,000 on a $10,000 investment.

Benjamin Franklin once said that a man has three great friends: an old wife, an old dog and compound interest. Now we can say a person has three great friends: a modest initial investment, time and compound interest.

# Follow investment professionals like sheep?

Axioms based on experience of professionals, not on mathematical theories.

**Don't put all your eggs in one basket.**

You can spread the risk by putting your money to work in different investments types — shares, managed funds, property, bonds and collectibles such as art and antiques.

You can reduce the risk further by widely spreading within each investment type. For example, you can diversify investment in shares by investing in national shares, international shares, industrial shares, resources shares, large 'blue chip' company shares and small company shares.

**Past performance is not an indicator of future performance**

Most financial institutions advise that caution should be exercised in relying upon past performance as an indicator of future performance.

**Don't follow a particular investor or friend like a sheep**

Warren Buffett, the legendary American investor and one of the world's richest men, is Chairman of Berkshire Hathaway Inc. His annual Letter to the Shareholders of Berkshire Hathaway provides an insight into his investing philosophy.

In one of these letters Buffett relates an anecdote told in the 1950s by Benjamin Graham, his teacher and mentor at Columbia Business School. The anecdote goes something like this:

An oil prospector, moving to his heavenly reward, was met by St Peter with bad news. 'You're qualified for residence,' said St Peter, but, as you can see, the compound reserved for oil men is packed. There's no way to squeeze you in.'

After thinking a moment, the prospector asked if he might

say just four words to present occupants. That seemed harmless to St Peter, so the prospector cupped his hands and yelled, 'Oil discovered in hell.'

Immediately, the gate to the compound opened and all of the oil men marched out to head for the nether region. Impressed, St Peter invited the prospector to move in and make himself comfortable. The prospector paused. 'No,' he said, 'I think I'll go along with the rest of the boys. There might be some truth to that rumour after all.'

The moral of this story: Make your investment decision based on your circumstances and advice from investment professionals, but don't follow a particular investor or friend like a sheep.

# Friday the 13th

The idea of lucky and unlucky numbers is deeply rooted
in history.

The sixth-century BC mathematician Pythagoras may have started the superstition of numbers. Besides geometrical figures, numbers also fascinated him. Some of his pupils formed themselves into a brotherhood for continuing his ideas. They called themselves Pythagoreans who considered that numbers ruled the universe. To them every number appeared to have been endowed with its own peculiar quality and character. They considered even numbers feminine and odd numbers masculine. They associated the number 1 with reason, 2 with opinion, 3 with mystery, 4 with justice, 5 with marriage, and so on. Relics of these fanciful ideas are still present in our language. For example, four dots form a square, and so a 'square deal' means justice.

The number philosophy of Pythagoreans was later divided into two streams — number theory and numerology. As astrology has no relation with modern astronomy, similarly numerology has nothing to do with modern number theories. Numerology — a system that uses names and birth dates to reveal character traits and predict the future — is based on absolutely fanciful ideas, and the characteristics attributed to numbers are both arbitrary and personal.

To some Friday the 13th is the confluence of the unluckiest of days and the unluckiest of numbers. Psychologists will tell you that if you fear the Friday the 13th you may suffer from paraskevidekatriaphobia. The symptoms of this phobia range from mild anxiety to panic attacks. In the Gregorian calendar, there is always at least one Friday the 13th during the year and never more than three. A comforting fact if you suffer from paraskevidekatriaphobia.

# Playing the odds

To win it you have to be in it.

The probability of selecting a ball with a certain number, say 12, at random from a box containing 45 balls numbered 1 to 45, is 1/45. If you have to randomly select six balls, the odds increase to 1 in about 8 million.

The odds increase to 1 in about 14 million if you have to randomly pick six balls from a box containing 49 numbered balls, and to 1 in 19 million if the box has 51 balls. Even though the odds are stacked against them, millions of people buy lottery tickets every day.

The Roman Emperor Augustus Caesar probably conducted the first public lottery for a community cause, raising funds for repair work in the city of Rome. These lotteries were simple as they involved drawing a number from a few hundred or a few thousand. State lotteries these days are complex affairs. Here are some of the myths of modern lotteries.

## You are more likely to be killed by lightning than win a lottery

The odds of being hit by lightning are estimated to be about 10.5 million to one. Winning a jackpot, therefore, is not that much easier. However, lotteries offer one advantage: there is no second prize in lightning strike. Lotteries do offer smaller prizes where the odds are much shorter.

## The larger the jackpot, the poorer the odds of winning

The odds of winning a lottery never change. But it is possible that because of a large jackpot, more people will buy tickets. This will increase the odds of sharing the jackpot.

## There are lucky numbers and unlucky numbers

Every number has the same chance of being drawn. Even 'strange' combinations such as

145

1, 2, 3, 4, 5, 6 have the same chances of winning as any other combination, say, 5, 12, 29, 31, 38, 40. Some newspapers publish lists and charts of the frequency of numbers drawn.

But, according to the theory of probability, these calculations are meaningless. It is a waste of time to use past numbers to predict future ones. Similarly, there are no 'hot' (a number that come up in the past few draws) or 'due' (a number that has not appeared for a while) numbers.

## Lottery systems can help you pick the winning numbers

There are no lottery systems or winning strategies that can help you win the jackpot. If there were such systems all mathematicians would be very wealthy people. They would not be teaching in schools or colleges.

Do not waste time on 'killer strategies' that promise 'to give you an edge over people who just randomly pick numbers or even worse buy computer-generated quick picks'. No computer, no fancy formula, no book can help you change the odds of winning a lottery.

## You can improve your chances of winning in a particular lottery by buying more tickets

In fact, more tickets you buy the more money you lose.

### Lotteries are investment

Dr Fred M. Hoppe, a Canadian professor of mathematics and statistics, has come up with some interesting calculations. He says that if a person spends $25 a week on Canada's Lotto 6/49 over 20 years, they could expect to lose $13,000 of their $24,000 investment. Over 20 years, the person could expect to win about 459 fifth-place prizes of $10 and 25 fourth-place prizes averaging $73.50.

The chances of winning the big prizes are slim: 0.47 third-place prizes of $2,300, 0.01 second-place prizes of $131,934 and 0.00185 jackpot prizes of $2.2 million. 'These numbers are averages, or expectations, rather than certainties,' he warns. If that person invests $25 a week (or $100 a month) in a managed fund and the average rate of return is 12% per annum compounded monthly, then they would collect $98,925 after 20 years.

See also PROBABILITY THEORY, p. 75.

# Take this simple test...

... to determine how rational you are.

Imagine a wealthy uncle offers you a choice of (a) or (b):

- (a) $1 million in cash
- (b) a 10% chance of receiving $5 million, an 89% chance of receiving $1 million and a 1% chance of receiving nothing

And a wealthy aunt offers you a choice of (c) or (d):

- (c) an 11% chance of receiving $1 million, and an 89% chance of receiving nothing
- (d) a 10% chance of receiving $5 million, and a 90% chance of receiving nothing

In each case, what offer would you choose?

A similar problem was posed in 1951 by the French economist Maurice Allais (b. 1911) who won the 1988 Nobel Prize for economics. Survey data collected by him, and confirmed by subsequent researchers, show that people prefer (a) to (b) and (d) to (c).

In the case of uncle's offer the expected value of (a) is $1 million while the expected value of (b) is $1.39 million. This means people are maximising expected utility, not expected value. In the case of aunt's offer the expected value of (c) is $110,000, while the expected value of (d) is $500,000. If people are preferring (d) to (c), they are maximising expected value, because the chances of winning are nearly the same in both cases but the amount is much large in (d) than in (c). People's choice of uncle's offer is inconsistent with their choice of aunt's offer. This is the paradox.

The paradox is a counter example of the independent axiom that rational choice between two alternatives should depend only on how those alternatives differ.

147

## Body-Mass Index (BMI)

# The honest scale

BMI is a measurement of body mass based on a person's height.

The eminent science writer Arthur C. Clarke once said: 'The best measure of a man's honesty isn't his income tax return. It's the zero adjust on his bathroom scale.' •

Knowing your body-mass index (BMI) can give you an idea of how healthy your weight is (without adjusting your bathroom scale). It is calculated by dividing weight in kilograms by the square of height in metres. If, for example, your weight is 60 kilograms and height 1.65 metres, press the following keys on a calculator: 60 [÷] 1.65 [÷] 1.65 [=]. The answer is 22.0.

Use the following formula for pounds and inches:

BMI:

$$\left(\frac{\text{weight in pounds}}{\text{height in inches} \times \text{height in inches}}\right) \times 703$$

If for example, your weight is 205 pounds and you're 5 feet 11 inches (that is, 71 inches) tall, press the following keys on a calculator: 205 [÷] 71 [÷] 71 [×] 703. The answer is 28.6 (see rounding off, p. 164, if you do not know how numbers are rounded off).

BMI for adults:
*underweight* — less than 18.5;
recommended — 18.5 to 24.9;
*overweight*— between 25 and 29.9;
*obese* — more than 30.

# Numbers near to your heart

The knowledge of the simple maths of cholesterol level and blood pressure can save lives.

**Cholesterol level**

'Watch your blood cholesterol,' is the mantra physicians preach to their older patients. Too much cholesterol in our bloodstream causes atherosclerosis, or hardening of the arteries, which is responsible for a large proportion of heart attacks.

There are two types of cholesterol: LDL (low density lipoprotein) is called 'bad' cholesterol because it is deposited on the artery walls and clogs them; HDL (high density lipoprotein) is called 'good' cholesterol because it unclogs the arteries. The higher your LDL level, the higher your risk of heart disease. But the higher your HDL level, the better.

When we talk about cholesterol levels, we usually mean total blood cholesterol. It is the most common measurement of blood cholesterol; it is measured in the US in milligrams per decilitre of blood (mg/dL). In some countries cholesterol is measured in millimole per litre of blood (mmol/L).

The following figures are for total blood cholesterol in adults: they are approximate and depend on other risk factors such as family history, obesity, high blood pressure, smoking and any history of heart attacks or stroke.

| Category | Total cholesterol level (in mg/dL – units used in the US) | Total cholesterol level (in mmol/L) |
|---|---|---|
| Desirable | Below 200 | Below 5.5 |
| Borderline-high | 200 to 239 | 5.5 and 6.5 |
| High | Above 240 | Above 6.5 |

A person with a 'high' level of cholesterol has more than the risk of heart disease compared with someone whose cholesterol level is at 'desirable level'.

**Blood pressure**

Hypertension, or high blood pressure, is called a 'silent killer' because people cannot sense or realise its symptoms. The chances of hypertension in a person rise with age, becoming more common after 35.

Blood pressure is the pressure exerted by blood in arteries. It is measured in millimetres of mercury (mm Hg). Blood pressure is always expressed in two numbers that represent systolic and diastolic pressures.

Systolic is the pressure when the heart muscles contract and blood flows into the arteries. Diastolic is the pressure when the heart muscles relax and the heart fills with blood from the veins. The blood pressure readings are always written one above the other, with the systolic number on the top and the diastolic number on the bottom. For example, 120/80 (120 over 80) mm Hg. Normal blood pressure (in mm HG) for adults are shown below.

| Category | Systolic | Diastolic |
|---|---|---|
| Optimal | < 120 | < 80 |
| Normal | < 130 | < 85 |
| High Normal | 130-139 | 85-90 |
| Hypertension Stage 1 Stage 2 Stage 3 | 140-159 160-179 > 180 | 90-99 100-109 > 110 |

## Maths of high-heel shoes

# How to stay upright

A little knowledge of algebra will help you if you're a fan of high heels.

Helpful boffins at the prestigious Institute of Physics, a scientific organisation with worldwide membership, have devised a tongue-in-cheek formula to help women work out how high their heels can go before they topple over or suffer agonies. The formula is:

$$h = Q \times (12 + 3s/8)$$

where $h$ is the maximum height of the heel in centimetres, $Q$ is a sociological factor and has a value between 0 and 1, and $s$ is the shoe size.

$Q$, the sociological factor, is determined by a complex formula based on other factors such as the number of years' experience wearing towering heels (as you become more adept, you can wear a higher heel), the cost of the shoe (clearly if the shoes are particularly expensive, you can put up with a higher heel!), time elapsed since the shoes were at the height of fashion (if the shoes are terribly fashionable, you should be prepared to put up with a little pain), and the number of social cocktails you plan to imbibe (so that you can give yourself a little leeway for reduced coordination). $Q$ also includes the probability that wearing the shoes will help you 'pull' (in a range from 0 to 1, where 1 is pwhooar and 0 is stick to carpet slippers). 'If the shoes are a turn-off, there's no point wearing them,' the boffins advise.

Another scientific study, conducted by Maria Cerruto of the University of Verona in Italy, has showed that moderately high-heeled shoes are not as bad for women's health as some suggest. 'Heels work the pelvic muscles and reduce the need to exercise them,' Cerruto says. 'Wearing heels during daily activity may reduce the need for pelvic floor exercises necessary to keep that part of a woman's anatomy toned and elastic.' Her findings are based on a study of 66 women under 50 who held their feet at an angle of 15° to the ground — equivalent to five-centimetre (two-inch) heels. Experts on women's shoes advise that heels should always be less than 11.5 centimetres (4.5 inches) high. Anything over is bad for posture.

## Maths of carbon footprint

# 'One must care about a world one will not see'

**A carbon footprint is a measure of the impact of human activities on the environment in terms of the amount of carbon dioxide ($CO_2$) and other greenhouse gases produced. It's measured in units of $CO_2$.**

Your personal carbon footprint is the direct effect your lifestyle has on the environment.

Your travel needs and electricity use at home are probably the biggest direct contributors to your personal carbon footprint. Clothes you wear, food you eat and many other activities contribute indirectly to your personal carbon footprint. It has been estimated that the average individual carbon footprint in the developed world is 9,700 kilograms $CO_2$ per person per year.

The Intergovernmental Panel on Climate Change, which shared the 2007 Nobel Peace Prize with Al Gore, has warned that we can no longer ignore the evidence that human activities are causing global warming: 'There is new and stronger evidence that most of the warming observed over the last fifty years is attributable to human activities.'

The Panel projects that our planet will warm between 1.1°C and 6.4°c this century, sea level rises will range from 18 to 59 centimetres by 2100, and there is at least 90 per cent probability that extremes such as heat waves and heavy rains will become more frequent.

Mahatma Gandhi (1869-1948) once said: 'One must care about a world one will not see.' If we want to save our planet, we all must do our bit to reduce greenhouse gases which cause global warming. Even simple steps — such as using compact fluorescent globes; recycling household waste, turning down your refrigerator, planting shade trees, insulating walls and ceilings in your house, and where possible walking or cycling instead of driving — can help reduce carbon emissions. You can use the following table to work out a personal plan to reduce your carbon footprint:

| Your carbon footprint when you use: | |
| --- | --- |
| 1 kWh (or 'unit') of electricity | 0.43 kg of $CO_2$ |
| 1 kWh (or 'unit' of gas) | 0.19 kg of $CO_2$ |
| 1 litre of petrol | 2.31 kg of $CO_2$ |
| 1 km of rail travel | 0.049 kg of $CO_2$ |
| 1 km of bus travel | 0.1 kg of $CO_2$ |
| 1 km of air travel | 0.3 kg of $CO_2$ |

Source: *How to Live a Low-Carbon Life* (Earthscan, 2007)

# A very brief history of mathematics

Unlike its weighty counterparts, Stephen Hawking's *A Brief History of Time* and Bill Bryson's *A Short History of Nearly Everything*, this history is a bit lightweight.

Arithmetic, algebra, geometry
　　Taught in schools
Was known
　　Centuries Ago;
And even the
　　Usual College course
Dates back
　　Three Hundred Years,
For analytics was created by Descartes
　　And calculus by Newton,
Both in the 17th century.

And yet the fact is
　　That mathematics,
Even To A Greater Extent Than Science,
　　Has moved steadily forward
Since that time.

— Lillian R. Lieber, *Galois and the Theory of Groups* (1932)

I cannot do't without counters.

— Clown to Autolycus in
William Shakespeare's
*The Winter's Tale*, Act IV, Scene III, in First Folio (1623)

*Note:* Now Clown won't be able to do it without calculators or computers,
mathematics, that is.

**The progression of mathematics ideas**

*Plato:* God ever geometrizes.
*Jacobi:* God ever arithmetizes.
*Dedekind:* Man ever arithmetizes.
*Cantor:* The essence of mathematics is in its freedom.

— Miriam H. Young in
*Arithmetic Teacher* (May 1964)

*Note:* Plato (*c.* 429-*c.* 347 BC);
Carl Jacobi (1804-1851):
Richard Dedekind (1831-1916);
Georg Cantor (1845-1918)

A Russian peasant came to Moscow for the first time... He went to the zoo and saw giraffes. You may find a moral in his reaction... 'Look,' he said, 'at what the Bolsheviks have done to our horses.' That is what modern mathematics has done to simple geometry and simple arithmetic.

— Edward Kasner and
James R. Newman,
*Mathematics and the Imagination* (1940)

Numbers written on restaurant bills within the confines of restaurants do not follow the same mathematical laws as numbers written on any other pieces of paper in any other parts of the Universe. This single statement took the scientific world by storm. It completely revolutionized it. So many mathematical conferences got held in such good restaurants that many of the finest minds of a generation died of obesity and heart failure and the science of math was put back by years.

— Douglas Adams, *Life, the Universe and Everything* (1982)

## Mathematics as a career

# So you want to be a mathematician?

### Advice from experts, verbatim!

Keep your mind open, but not so open that your brains fall out.

— Ian Stewart, *Letters to a Young Mathematician* (2006)

The best way to do mathematics is to do mathematics... The reader is urged to acquire the habit of reading with paper and pencil in hand; in this way mathematics will become increasingly meaningful to him.

— József Kürschák, *Hungarian Problem Book I* (English translation, 1963)

The clearer the teacher makes it, the worse it is for you. You must work things out for yourself and make the ideas your own.

— William F. Osgood in *American Mathematics Monthly* (December 1984)

To be a scholar of mathematics you must be born with talent, insight, concentration, taste, luck, drive and the ability to visualize and guess.

— Paul R. Halmos, *I Want to be a Mathematician* (1985)

## Edmund Landau

# 'Forget everything you have learned in school'

### A few words of advice from a master mathematician.

The German mathematician Edmund Landau (1877-1938) was a pure mathematician whose main area of interest was number theory (see p. 82).

His works are beyond the scope of this book and he appears here for a unique preface he wrote for one of his textbooks. He had a distinct style of writing which he himself described as 'merciless telegram style'.

Landau wrote many books on higher mathematics, but the one that interests us is *Grundlagen der Analysis* (1930), which appeared in English translation in 1950 as *Foundations of Analysis*. In this book he wrote two prefaces, one for students and the other for teachers. The preface for students begins with:

1. Please don't read the preface for the teacher.

2. I will ask of you only the ability to read English and to think logically — no high school mathematics, and certainly no higher mathematics.

3. Please forget everything you have learned in school; for you haven't learned it.

4. The multiplication table will not occur in this book, not even the theorem.

$$2 \times 2 = 4,$$

but I would recommend, as an exercise, that you define

$$2 = 1 + 1,$$
$$4 = (((1 + 1) + 1) + 1),$$

and then prove the theorem.

The preface for the teacher ends with the words:

I hope that I have written this book in such a way that a normal student can read it in two days. And then (since he already knows the formal rules from school) he may forget its content.

# When xxx does not mean xxx

Knowledge of Roman numerals may help you to decipher something like MCMLXXX on a majestic monument or the credits at the end of a movie.

The Roman numerals are represented by seven capital letters of the alphabet:

I    one
V    five
X    ten
L    fifty
C    one hundred
D    five hundred
M    one thousand

There are two main rules: (a) when a numeral symbol is preceded by one of the lesser value, subtract that value to give the number; (b) when the symbol is followed by another of less or equal value, add them together. The number 4 is sometimes written as IIII (such as on the dials of clocks), and 400 as CCCC.

| 1 | 2 | 3 | 4 | 5 | 6 | 7 |
|---|---|---|---|---|---|---|
| I | II | III | IV | V | VI | VII |
| 8 | 9 | 10 | 25 | 50 | 65 | 90 |
| VIII | IX | X | XXV | L | LXV | XC |
| 100 | 350 | 500 | 800 | 900 | 1000 | 2000 |
| C | CCCL | D | DCCC | CM | M | MM |

# A day for any date

An easy way to find out the day of the week a certain event took place or will take place.

Follow these simple steps:

1. Take the last two digits in the year (let's take Einstein's birth date 14 March 1879 as an example; the last two digits are 79).

2. Divide this number by 4, discard any remainder. Add this number to the number in step 1 (79 ÷ 4 = 19 if we ignore the remainder; 19 + 79 = 98).

3. From Table 1 find the month number and add this number to the sum of step 2 (the month number for March is 4 and 4 + 98 = 102).

4. Divide the sum of step 3 by 7, note the remainder number, if the remainder is 0, use 7 as the remainder number (102 ÷ 7, the remainder is 4).

5. Find the century number from Table 2 and add it to the sum of step 4 (the century number for 1879 is 2 and 4 + 2 = 6).

6. The sum of step 5 tells you the day of the week, which you can find in Table 3 (Einstein was born on a Friday).

The above steps can be compressed into a complex formula which is known as Zeller's formula after its inventor, Christian Zeller (1824-99), a German mathematician and clergyman.

| Table 1. Month numbers | |
| --- | --- |
| January | 1 |
| February | 4 |
| March | 4 |
| April | 0 |
| May | 2 |
| June | 5 |
| July | 0 |
| August | 3 |
| September | 6 |
| October | 1 |
| November | 4 |
| December | 6 |

For leap years, January is 0 and February 3 (1800 and 1900 were not leap years but 2000 was)

| Table 2. Century numbers | |
| --- | --- |
| 1700 to 1799 | 4 |
| 1800 to 1899 | 2 |
| 1900 to 1999 | 0 |
| 2000 to 2099 | 6 |
| 2100 to 2199 | 4 |

These numbers are for Gregorian calendar (see p. 50) only

| Table 3. Day numbers | |
| --- | --- |
| Sunday | 1 |
| Monday | 2 |
| Tuesday | 3 |
| Wednesday | 4 |
| Thursday | 5 |
| Friday | 6 |
| Saturday | 7 |

# Scientific notation

# Powers of ten

Rule for using powers of 10 in scientific notation (and in a highly unscientific method of describing trivia).

In science we deal with very large and very small numbers, which are inconvenient to read and difficult to compare.

To overcome this difficulty we use powers of 10. In this notation a number is expressed in the form $N \times 10^m$, where $N$ is a number between 1 and 10 and $m$ is the appropriate power (exponent). For example:

| Number | Scientific notation |
|---|---|
| 1 | $1 \times 10^0$ |
| 10 | $1 \times 10^1$ |
| 100 | $1 \times 10^2$ |
| 1000 | $1 \times 10^3$ |
| 10,000 | $1 \times 10^4$ |
| 0.1 | $1 \times 10^{-1}$ |
| 0.01 | $1 \times 10^{-2}$ |
| 0.001 | $1 \times 10^{-3}$ |
| 0.0001 | $1 \times 10^{-4}$ |
| 0.00001 | $1 \times 10^{-5}$ |

**Prefixes for power of ten**

| Prefix | Abbreviation | Multiple |
|--------|--------------|----------|
| yotta- | Y | $10^{24}$ |
| zeta- | Z | $10^{21}$ |
| exa- | E | $10^{18}$ |
| peta- | P | $10^{15}$ |
| tera- | T | $10^{12}$ |
| giga- | G | $10^{9}$ |
| mega- | M | $10^{6}$ |
| kilo- | k | $10^{3}$ |
| hecto- | h | $10^{2}$ |
| deka-, deca- | da | $10$ |
| deci- | d | $10^{-1}$ |
| centi- | c | $10^{-2}$ |
| milli- | m | $10^{-3}$ |
| micro- | $\mu$ (mu) | $10^{-6}$ |
| nano- | n | $10^{-9}$ |
| pico- | p | $10^{-12}$ |
| femto- | f | $10^{-15}$ |
| atto- | a | $10^{-18}$ |
| zepto- | z | $10^{-21}$ |
| yocto- | y | $10^{-24}$ |

In computer data storage, kilo- is applied to base-2, not 10, and denotes $2^{10}$ (= 1024). Similarly, mega-, giga- and tera- are applied to base -2 and denotes $2^{20}$ (= 1,048,576), $2^{30}$ (= 1,073,741,824) and $10^{40}$ (= 1,099,511,627,776) respectively.

## Order of magnitude

The order of magnitude is the power of 10 that shows the relative sizes of numbers. For example, a dollar (= 100¢ = $10^2$¢) is two orders of magnitude more valuable than one cent. Orders of magnitude provide an easy way to compare measurements. For example, when rounded off to the nearest power of 10, the masses of the Earth and the electron are $10^{25}$ and $10^{-30}$ kg respectively, or the Earth is 55 orders of magnitude more massive than the electron.

## Significant numbers

The accurately known digits in a calculated number are known as significant figures. For example, 672,584; 4,563,269; and 0.00520927 reduced to four significant figures become 672,600; 4,563,000 and 0.005209. The result of a calculation never has more significant figures than the input data. If, for example, in a calculation $\pi = 3.14$, then the answer cannot have more than three significant figures. The rules for writing significant figures are:

- All nonzero digits are significant: 24.5 has three significant figures.

- All zero and nonzero digits in the base number of scientific notation are significant: 2.10 × $10^2$ has three significant figures.

- In numbers less than 1, zeros on the right of a decimal point are not significant: 0.004 has one significant figure.

- When a zero appears between two nonzero numbers, it is

163

significant: 10.2 has three significant numbers.

- Zeros to the right of a decimal point and to the right of a nonzero digit are significant: 34.230 has five significant figures.

**Rounding off**

Follow this simple rule for rounding off a number: if the first digit after the one being rounded off is 5 or more than 5, increase the digit to the left by one. If it is less than 5, leave it as it is. For example, if the interest payment by a bank is calculated $42.5683, it must be rounded off to the nearest cent. As '6' in the cents position is followed by an '8', '6' should be rounded up to a '7', making the interest payment $42.57. Similarly, 75,643 can be rounded off to 75,640 (nearest ten) or 75,600

(nearest hundred) or 76,000 (nearest thousand).

**Trivial prefixes**

The following 'Standards for Inconsequential Trivia' by Philip A Simpson first appeared in *The NBS Standard* (January 1970). Use them with a grain of salt.

| | |
|---|---|
| $10^{-15}$ bismol | = 1 femto-bismol |
| $10^{-12}$ boos | = 1 picoboo |
| 1 boo$^2$ | = a boo boo |
| $10^{-18}$ boys | = 1 attoboy |
| $10^{12}$ bulls | = 1 terabull |
| $10^1$ cards | = 1 decacards |
| $10^{-9}$ goats | = a nanogoat |
| 2 gorics | = 1 paregoric |
| $10^{-3}$ ink machines | = 1 millink machine |
| $10^9$ los | = 1 gigalo |
| $1^{-1}$ mate | = 1 decimate |
| $10^{-2}$ mental | = 1 centimental |
| $1^{-2}$ pedes | = 1 centipede |
| $10^6$ phones | = 1 megapone |
| $10^{-6}$ phones | = 1 microphone |
| $10^{12}$ pins | = 1 terapin |

# At the dinner table

Bored? You may yawn now... and then try these puzzles.

In everyday life yawning is a sign of boredom, fatigue or drowsiness. It's more common during the hour before bedtime and the hour after waking.

It is also 'contagious': 55 per cent of people will yawn within five minutes of seeing someone else yawn. Luckily, the life span of average yawn is only six seconds. These are some of the facts about yawning.

Now back to mathematics. Plato (see p. 32) has said: 'Mathematics is like chequers in being suitable for the young, not too difficult, amusing and without peril to the state.' Plato would have approved mathematical games and puzzles at any dinner table.

With the following activities you can amuse yourself quietly at your dinner table without any paper or pencil and without putting yourself in peril to the state (or family) by discussing politics of the state (or family). The activities may seem simple but require lateral thinking or, as they say, thinking outside the square.

### Moving glasses

Six glasses are placed in a row. The first three are empty. The last three are filled with water. (1) You can move two glasses at a time and close together so that the thumb and finger pick them up both. In three moves, can you arrange them so that the full glasses and empty ones alternate? (2) By moving only one glass, can you arrange them so that the full glasses and empty ones alternate?

## Coffee pots

These two coffee pots are of the same width, but the pot on the left is taller. Which pot will hold more coffee?

## Water jugs

One jug has a 3-litre capacity and the other 5-litre capacity. Can you fill one jug with 4 litres of water?

## Twelve toothpicks

Twelve toothpicks are placed on the table to form four squares. Remove two toothpicks and leave only two squares.

## Four toothpicks and a coin

Four toothpicks and a coin are arranged to represent an olive in a wine glass. Move two toothpicks (not the coin) in such a way that you have a similar wine glass but without the olive.

Answers to these puzzles can be found on page 168.

166

# Answers to puzzles

**Page 31. Mother Goose rhyme**
One or nine depending on how you interpret it.

**Page 99. Ten weary, footsore travellers**
There are only nine guests. One of the two guests initially placed in Room A, let's say 'the first guest', and then transferred to Room I has been treated as if he were also 'the tenth guest'.

**Page 105: Trick donkeys**

Picture from *Sam Loyd's Cyclopedia of puzzles* (1914)

**Page 106: The spider and the fly**
The answer is 40 feet. The diagram of the unfolded room below explains it all. (It uses a 3-4-5 triangle.)

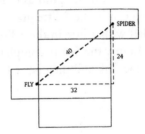

**Page 132: Cryptoarithmetic puzzles**

$$\begin{array}{r} 2\,8\,6 \\ +\,2\,8\,6 \\ \hline 5\,7\,2 \end{array}$$

$$\begin{array}{r} 2\,9\,7\,8\,6 \\ +\quad\ 8\,5\,0 \\ +\quad\ 8\,5\,0 \\ \hline 3\,1\,4\,8\,6 \end{array}$$

Other solutions are also possible.

### Page 165: Moving glasses

1. Move glasses 1 and 2 to the end of line beyond glass 6, then move glasses 1 and 6 beyond glass 2 and then fill the gap with glasses 3 and 4.

2. Pour the contents of glass 5 into glass 2.

### Page 166: Coffee pots

Both will hold the same volume of coffee because their spouts are at the same level.

### Page 166: Water jug

Fill the 3-litre jug and pour it into the 5-litre jug. Fill the 3-litre jug again and pour as much as you can in the 5-litre jug. You are left with 1 litre in the 3-litre jug. Empty the 5-litre completely into the sink and then pour 1 litre from the 3-litre jug. Fill the 3-litre jug and pour it into the 5-litre jug. You have now 4 litres in the 5-litre jug.

### Page 166: Twelve toothpicks

Move any two inside toothpicks that meet at right angles. You are left with one small square inside a large square.

### Page 166: Four toothpicks and a coin

Slide the horizontal toothpick towards the right so that its centre touches the top-right toothpick. Now move the top-left toothpick parallel to the existing bottom toothpick. You will have an upside wine glass with the olive outside it.

□ □ □